<u>Hillside Flower Show. 1934.</u>

Prize for the best garden awarded to :—

M. B. HULL.

Presented by Comdr F. D. Butt.

BIRDS IN FLIGHT

Uniform with this Volume

BIRDS
AND THEIR YOUNG

BY

T. A. COWARD, M.Sc.

Illustrated by

ROLAND GREEN, F.Z.S

Containing 12 plates in colour and 32 plates
in black and white

BIRDS
ONE SHOULD KNOW
BENEFICIAL AND MISCHIEVOUS

BY

THE REV. CANON THEODORE WOOD

Illustrated by

ROLAND GREEN, F.Z.S.

Containing 8 plates in colour and 16 plates
in black and white

Roland Green

Kingfisher and Young

BIRDS IN FLIGHT

BY

W. P. PYCRAFT, F.Z.S.

Zoological Department, British Museum (Natural History)
Fellow of the Zoological Society of London
Hon. Member of the American Ornithologists' Union
Associate of the Linnean Society
Member of the Marine Biological Association of the United Kingdom
Member of the Royal Anthropological Institute

Author of " A History of Birds " " The Infancy of Animals "
" The Courtship of Animals " " The Sea-shore " Etc. Etc. Etc.

Illustrated by

ROLAND GREEN, F.Z.S.

LONDON
GAY & HANCOCK LIMITED
1922
All Rights Reserved

CONTENTS

CONTENTS

ILLUSTRATIONS

Coloured Plates

Black and White Plates

ILLUSTRATIONS

Line Illustrations

viii

PREFACE

THERE are hosts of people who have a genuine love of our native birds without yearning to possess their skins, or desiring to acquire the reputation of being "Ornithologists." They would call them all by name if they could, but seek, alas! in vain, for some book wherein they will find some magic phrase which will enable them to identify every bird they meet by the wayside.

Most of our native birds have learnt that "discretion is the better part of valour," when in the neighbourhood of Man. Hence one gets but too often no more than a fleeting glance at their retreating forms, which, from frequent encounters, have become familiar, yet they leave no more than a vague image in the memory. "What bird *was* that? I have often seen it but have never succeeded in taking it unawares." This is a question, and its comment, often put to me.

Those who are in this quandary, and they are many, are always hoping to find some book which will enable them to correctly name the retreating forms. That book will never be written. In the following pages an attempt is made to aid such inquirers, and at the same time the difficulties of the task are pointed out.

It is hoped, however, that this attempt will find a welcome among those for whom it is made. If it helps them to understand something, at least, of the absorbing and fascinating problems which the study of flight in the animal kingdom presents, it will at least have served some useful purpose.

The pursuit of the flying bird will inevitably stimulate a desire to know more about the bewildering changes of plumage presented at different seasons of the year, as well as by the striking differences which often distinguish the two sexes, and the immature birds. The endeavour to satisfy this desire will open up a new world. Those who would pass to this knowledge should possess themselves of the *Practical Handbook of British Birds*. Though most severely practical, and designed for the serious student alone, even the beginner will find interest in the description of these several plumages, and much else beside that it is essential to know.

Now that the study of flight is so much to the fore, some may turn to these pages in the hope of gaining useful information on the theme of mechanical flight. Some help they may find. But it was not for this that they were written. The flight of an aeroplane and the flight of a bird have little in common—at present ; though something may be learned by the study of gliding flight and soaring, which of course have their place in this book. But anatomical details and mechanical formulæ, necessary to the serious student of flight, would have been entirely out of place here, and they have been omitted.

My task has been by no means easy. But it has been enormously helped by the extremely skilful and beautiful work of the artist, Mr. Roland Green. Where birds are concerned, few artists in the past, and very few in the present, have shown any ability to combine accuracy in drawing with ingenuity of composition and faithfulness in colouring. Mr. Green has shown this rare combination ; his coloured plates and line-drawings speak for themselves.

W. P. PYCRAFT.

LONDON,
September 1922.

x

CHAPTER I

Concerning Wings

"Divinity within them breeding wings
wherewith to scorn the earth."
MILTON.

What a wing is—The quill feathers and their function—The skeleton of the wing—The muscles of the wing—The great air-chambers of the body—The bat's wing—The wing of flying dragons—The wings of dragon-flies and beetles.

THE flight of birds has always aroused man's envy and stirred his imagination. David longed for the wings of a dove : the writer of the Book of Proverbs tells us that " the way of an eagle " surpasses his understanding. Icarus, spurred on by dire necessity, actually, we are told, contrived to fly—but his maiden effort ended in disaster ! To-day we have, in a sense, succeeded where he failed. But only because we have given up the idea of flight by personal effort, and make our aerial journeys in a flying machine.

That we owe much of our success to a study of the flight of birds is common knowledge, but the machine which has evolved as a consequence of this study pursues its way through the air after a very different fashion from that of the birds, for its vast body is thrust, or drawn, through the air by means

I

of a propeller, driven at incredible speed, its immobile wings sustaining the weight. The wings of the bird, on the other hand, not only lift the body from the earth, but they sustain it in the air by their marvellously complex movements. And this is true, in varying degrees of bird, and bat, and butterfly : of dragon-fly and beetle.

Even they who must perforce dwell in crowded cities see daily the miracle of flight performed. For even here sparrows and pigeons, at least, are everywhere, and it is just because this is so, just because they have become so " commonplace," that their very presence escapes notice. Yet the wonder of their movements in the air might become a never-ending source of delight if only we went about our business with open eyes and minds alert.

Watch the wary sparrow spring from the ground and dart across the road, or up to the nearest house-top. How is it done with such incredible speed and accuracy ?

To understand even the broad principles of flight, it is necessary to realize, at the very beginning, that the wing, in the case of the bird, or the bat, is a specially modified fore-leg. So also is the human arm and hand. But its transformation has not been so drastic as that of the bird, or the bat. Wherein the hand has been, as it were, completely re-modelled to fulfil the peculiar and complex functions demanded of it.

How should one describe the wing of a bird, as one sees it in flight ?

The Dictionary, obscure and inaccurate as Dictionaries usually are, defines a wing as " the organ of a bird, or other animal, or insect, by which it flies—any side-piece." Might not the impression one gathers of a wing, during flight, be defined as of a lateral extension of the body, presenting a relatively large surface, but having no appreciable thickness ? That surface, examined in a dead bird, is seen to be formed, for the most part, of a series of parallel, tapering, elastic rods, fringed with an innumerable series of smaller, similar, but much shorter rods, closely packed, and linked together by some invisible means to form an elastic web ? These we call the " quill," or " flight-feathers." The rest of the wing, and the body itself, is clothed with precisely similar structures, differing only in their smaller size. We call them " feathers " commonly, without realizing that they are the " Hall-mark " of the bird, for no other creature has ever been similarly clothed.

These quill-feathers play such a tremendously important part in flight that their arrangement and relation to the underlying skeleton must be carefully examined by all who would understand the flight of birds. To begin with, then, note that they are so arranged as to overlap one another, the free edges of the quills facing the outer edge of the wing.

3

Only by this arrangement would flight be possible, for on the upstroke of the wing through the air the quills act like the shutters of the sails of a windmill, allowing the wind to pass between them and so relieving pressure on the uplifting wing-stroke. On the down-stroke, the opposite effect is produced. The full force of the stroke is conserved, because, owing to the overlap, the several feathers are now pressed closely together to form an impervious sheet.

How are they fixed to the skeleton? To see this all the smaller feathers and the muscles, or "flesh" of the wing must be removed. It will then be found that the flight-feathers are divisible into two series. One, widely spaced, runs along the upper surface of the forearm: the other, closely packed, along what answers to the back of the hand. In effect this is but a single rod of bone, but it is composed of three elements, answering to three of the digits of the human hand—the thumb and the first and second fingers. But they are scarcely recognizable as such, for the thumb is reduced to a mere stump, while the two fingers have become welded together. The third finger, indeed, has become reduced to the palm-bone, and a short stump answering to the first finger-joint. To this frame-work, which can be folded up into the shape of a Z when the bird is at rest, the quills are fixed by their base by means of slender, but very strong elastic tendons. In birds which have a long upper arm-bone, like

SWANS   HERONS

GEESE

the Albatross, Gull, or Heron, there is a third series of long, almost "quill-like" feathers running from the elbow to the body, thus closing up what would otherwise be a gap between the wing surface and the body, rendering flight impossible.

The most important muscles of the wing are those which have to provide the power for the down-stroke of the wing. And these are the "pectoral" or "breast-muscles"—which form such dainty meat in a roast fowl. Owing to their great bulk the breast-bone itself would be insufficient to afford them attachment. This is furnished by the development of a deep, median keel, so that the breast-bone of a bird, such as a pigeon, bears a fanciful resemblance, when seen in profile, to the hull of a ship—unusually shallow—with a very deep keel. The front end of the breast-bone supports two slender rods of bone, and these in their turn support the long, sword-like blade-bone, and the "merry-thought."

The general appearance of this frame-work for the support of the wing and its muscles can be seen in the adjoining illustrations. But it must be remembered that in their relative sizes and disposition these various parts present a very considerable range of differences. That these differences are correlated with different forms of flight goes without saying, but, be it noted, no one, as yet, has attempted to discover in what way they are related. Some of the readers of this book may, perhaps, be tempted to try and solve the problems which these differences present. To begin with, a collection of breast-bones of different species of birds with their attached shoulder-girdles should be made, and these should be studied together with careful observations of the flight of the living bird. So far only a few comparisons of this kind have been made.

It must not be supposed that the whole secret of flight in birds is concentrated in the skeleton of the breast-bone and its shoulder-girdle, and the muscles attached thereto. But those who would investigate the modifications of the rest of the body which have taken place in harmony with the requirements of flight, must turn to more learned treatises. There is, however, one point which demands notice here. And this is the popular belief that birds have the power of materially reducing their weight when on the wing by drawing air into their lungs, and storing it in large air-chambers enclosed within the body. These chambers are indeed concerned with the needs of flight. But the precise part they play is yet to be discovered. They certainly have no effect of rendering the body lighter. So far as our knowledge goes it would seem that they act as regulators of the temperature and as reservoirs of breathing air, during the strenuous efforts of flight.

It is a mistake to suppose that it is unnecessary to consider other kinds of flight when studying that of birds. Even

Jays

those who are not interested in the abstruse problems of the mechanism of bird's flight, will find that comparisons made between birds, bats, butterflies, and beetles when on the wing are immensely interesting, and help to bring out the peculiarities of each.

During the twilight hours of a still summer evening one may compare, with advantage, the rushing swoop of the screaming swift, borne with lightning speed upon long, ribbon-like pinions, with the curiously erratic flight of the woolly bat with beaded eyes, who has ventured abroad for his evening meal. One cannot but feel astonishment at the marvellous dexterity with which he twists and turns, now shooting up into the sky, now darting downward. What bird can beat him, or even match him, in the art of doubling back on his tracks? And one can put his skill at lightning turns to the test if one attempts to catch him in a butterfly net. Often indeed have I attempted this feat, but never yet with success.

In the glare of noon-day this aerial athlete may perhaps be found in a deep slumber, hanging head downwards behind the shutters of a cottage window, or in some crevice of a barn-roof. Gently seize him and as gently stretch out his wing. The moment one opens it one sees that it is constructed upon a totally different plan from that of a bird. In the first place a thin membrane, or fold of skin, is seen to take the place of the series of quill-feathers found in the wing of the bird. In the second it will be found that this membrane is stretched between a series of long and very slender bony rods. These are excessively attenuated fingers. And if the hinder border of the wing-membrane be traced inwards it will be found to be attached to the hind limb. In some species it will be found that this membrane passes backwards beyond the leg to attach itself to the tail. Here, then, is a wing as efficient for its purpose as that of a bird, but constructed on a totally different plan.

Ages ago, before even the birds or the beasts had appeared on the earth, the winged dragons, which the Men of Science call Pterodactyles, held the proud position of being, not only the first, but the only creatures blessed with a backbone that could fly. Their wings resembled those of the bats, but differed in this, that instead of the wing-membrane being stretched between all the fingers, leaving only the thumb free, it was attached only to the fifth finger, leaving the remaining fingers free, and these were reduced to mere vestiges. As with the birds, the breast-bone was very broad and was furnished with a keel, while in the bats it takes the form of a joined rod, down which no more than a slight keel is ever developed.

But millions of years before the Flying-dragons, birds, and bats came into being, the stupendous problem of flight had been solved. Far away in the distant Devonian Epoch, when the distribution of land and water over the earth's surface was totally different from that of to-day, dragon-flies and caddis-flies disported themselves in the summer sun, amid landscapes that would seem strange to our eyes. For there were no trees and flowering plants, such as we know.

The dragon-flies of that remote epoch were very like those of to-day, whose dancing flights and graceful, swooping movements are such a delight to watch by reed-fringed pools, or river-banks, during the sweltering days of summer. This flight is very different from that of a bird, though it would be hard to say precisely in what it differs. But we have no such difficulty in regard to the broad outlines of the mechanism of such flight. To begin with there are two pairs of wings, and these appear to be fashioned out of some curiously gauze-like material, a sort of mesh-work tissue, often strikingly coloured. And they are obviously driven after a very different fashion from those of the bird. For in the bird they are moved by quivering muscles, attached to a bony, internal skeleton. In the dragon-fly—as with all insects—the hard skeleton, composed of a material known as "chitin," forms the outside of the body and encloses the muscles. Finally, for we may not dwell very long over this aspect of flight, it is clear that the wings cannot have been derived from modified fore-legs, like those of the bat, or the bird. Rather, it would seem, they have developed out of plate-like breathing organs.

The restful twilight hours of summer tempt not only bats from their hiding-places, but a host of other winged creatures which are rarely to be seen, or heard, during the glare of noon. Among these is the lumbering dor-beetle, who, with lazy drone steers clear of solid objects only with difficulty. Many, indeed, are his failures. He and his kin are no match for bats and owls, who find them juicy morsels! On the next opportunity catch one and examine him. His wings are curiously interesting. There are the usual two pairs: but the fore-wings have been changed to serve as covers for the hind-wings. During flight they are spread outwards, and indirectly, no doubt, assist flight. But the hind-wings are the real propellers. And it will be noticed that when not in use they can be folded up in a perfectly wonderful manner, so as to lie completely underneath the fore-wings, or " elytra," so that when the creature is crawling it appears to be wingless.

Now compare these with the transparent wings of the bee, or the gorgeously scale-covered wings of the butterfly. It is well worth while. If this examination be done very carefully, and with the aid of a magnifying glass, it will be found that the fore and hind wings are yoked together in the wing of the bee, by a delicate mechanism of hooks. In the moths, but not in the butterflies, a bristle, or sometimes two or three bristles, serve the same purpose. Further, in the case of the bee it will be found that the fore-wing, when at rest, is folded longitudinally back upon itself.

Finally, turn to the flies. Herein it will be seen that there is but a single pair of wings, the hind pair having become reduced to mere stumps, known as " balancers."

Much, very much more, might have been said of these wings : but our conversation is of birds. We cannot, however, properly appreciate either the essential characters of their wings, or their flight, without some such standards of comparison as is afforded by the wings of other creatures.

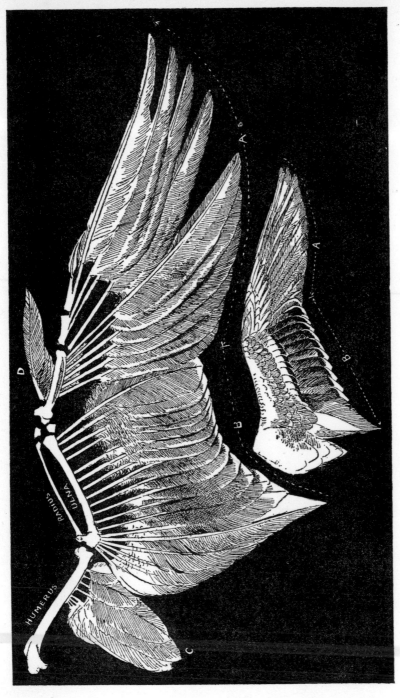

A PRIMARIES.   B SECONDARIES.   C TECTRICES.   D BASTARD WING.

The upper figure shows the under side of wing with the coverts removed to show attachment of flight feathers to skeleton.

The lower figure shows the quill or flight feathers and the coverts in their natural condition.

13

CHAPTER II

The First Bird

"And let Fowl fly above the earth; with wings
Displayed in the open firmament of heaven."
MILTON.

The ancestors of birds—The first known bird and its many remarkable features—The gradual evolution of the birds of to-day.

SOONER or later all bird-lovers find themselves pondering over the problem of the origin of birds: how they evolved their peculiar covering of feathers: what was the fashion of the original arm and hand out of which the wing was fashioned: and finally, whence have the birds been derived?

Since these pages are avowedly devoted to the subject of Flight, any attempt to summarize the state of our knowledge on these aspects of the history of birds would be in the nature of a trespass on the space, of necessity limited, which even a cursory survey of flight demands.

Let it suffice, then, to say that birds are descended from reptiles. The skeleton of modern birds bears undubitable testimony of this. For we have the evidence furnished us

15

by the remains of two remarkable skeletons, belonging to that very wonderful reptile-like bird, Archæopteryx.

Only two skeletons of this wonderful bird are known, and they were obtained, many years ago, from the Solenhofen, or Lithographic slates of Bavaria. The wing and tail feathers are as perfectly developed as in modern birds. But these precious fossils present two characters which have long since been lost by birds. The first of these is the presence of well-developed teeth in the jaws. The birds of to-day have horny beaks. The teeth bespeak the reptile. The second is the long, tapering tail, which is composed of a series of cylindrical bones, forming a lizard-like appendage. But each bone, be it noted, supported a pair of stiff tail-quills, so that the tail of this ancient bird, in its general appearance, differs in a very striking way from that of a modern bird, wherein these feathers seem all to spring from a common base, fan-wise. But as a matter of fact this appearance is deceptive, for the large bone, or " pygostyle " which supports the tail feathers of the adult, is found, in the embryo, to be made up of a series of separate pieces, agreeing in number with those of the tail of the fossil ancestor, Archæopteryx. Each of these separate bones has, in fact, in the course of the ages, been shortened up to the condition of mere discs ; and this " telescoping " of the vertebræ has brought the once separated feathers close up, so that their bases lie packed in like the spokes of a fan. As a result, a much more efficient tail for the needs of flight has come into being. And the tail, it must be remembered, plays, especially in some birds, an important part. But this is not all. We have now to consider the wing. In all essentials this agrees with that of living birds. And this agreement is strikingly close when it is compared with the embryonic and early nestling stages. A detailed account of these resemblances, and differences, would be out of place here. Suffice it to say that its closest modern counterparts are to be found in the wing of the nestling of that strange South American bird, the Hoatzin, and the " Game-birds," such as of a young pheasant, or a young fowl. The evidence these can furnish in this matter of the evolution of the birds' wing will be found in Chapter VI. For the moment it will be more profitable to discuss the broad outlines of the origin of flight, so far as this is possible.

On this theme there are, as might be supposed, many opinions—some of them bearing little relation to fact.

The feet of Archæopteryx, it is important to remember, bear a very extraordinary likeness to the feet of a " perching " bird, say that of a crow. They are without any semblance of doubt, the feet of a bird which lived in trees. Archæopteryx, then, was an arboreal bird. And this being so, the most reasonable hypothesis of the origin of flight is that it developed out of " gliding " movements, made for the purpose of passing

CHAPTER III

The Sizes and Shapes of Wings and their relation to Flight

" . . . the fowls of heaven have wings,
  And blasts of heaven will aid their flight :

Chains tie us down by land and sea.
                                    WORDSWORTH.

The evasiveness of flight—The size of the wing in relation to that of the body—
Noisy flight—"Muffled " flight—The swoop of the sparrow-hawk—The "flighting " of ducks—The autumn gatherings of starlings and swallows—"Soaring "
flights of storks and vultures—The wonderful "sailing " feats of the albatross—
The " soaring " of the skylark—The " plunging " flight of the gannet, tern, and
kingfisher.

WHO needs to be told that birds fly ? So commonplace has this fact become that the many and varied
forms of wings, and the peculiarities of flight which are
associated with these differences, are rarely perceived. Even
sculptors and artists show a hopeless unfamiliarity with the
shapes of wings, and their meanings, at any rate, as a general
rule. Look at their attempts to display birds in flight, or
in the fanciful use of wings which convention has ascribed to
angels. For the most part these superbly beautiful appendages are atrociously rendered.

21

Yet it must be confessed that any attempt to explain exactly how birds fly must fail. We can do no more than state the more obvious factors which are indispensable to flight, and the nature of its mechanism. The subtleties and delicate adjustments of actual flight evade us.

Our appreciation, however, of this supreme mode of locomotion will be materially quickened, if we make a point of studying the varied forms of flight as opportunities present themselves.

To begin with, it is worth noting that the size of the wing decreases with the weight of the body to be lifted—up to a certain point, of course. This, perhaps, may seem a strange statement to make. But it can be readily verified. Compare, for example, the size of the body in relation to the wings, in the case of the butterfly and the dragon-fly, on the one hand, and the partridge and the crow, on the other. The two first named, by comparison, have enormous wings.

Birds, it will be noticed, which haunt woods, or thickets, have short, rounded wings, like the wren, the pheasant, or the tawny owl. Such, on the other hand, as live in the open, like the gull, and the swallow, have long, pointed wings. The reason for this is fairly plain. Birds which must steer their course through the intricate mazes of a wood, or thicket, would find their flight seriously hampered by long wings.

Roland Gre

Pheasants

These general principles once realized, a foundation is laid on which one may base observations on the peculiarities of flight distinguishing different types of birds.

Most of us, probably, at one time or another, in taking a walk through the woods, have been startled, almost out of our wits, by a sudden " whirr " of wings at our very feet ; made by some crouching pheasant, waiting till the very last moment before revealing himself, by taking flight. This alarming noise is due to the shortness and stiffness of the quill, or flight-feathers. With pinions moving with incredible speed, the bird is off like a rocket. Not seldom, probably, it owes its life to this ability to disconcert its enemies, till it has put a safe distance between itself and danger. By way of contrast, let us take the absolutely silent, easy movements of the owl, stealing forth in the twilight of a summer's evening, seeking whom he may devour. Here, again, we have a meaning in the mode of flight. Here silence is more than golden : it means life itself. Nimble-footed, sharp-eared mice and rats, must be snatched up before even the breath of suspicion can reach them. The uncanny silence of this approach is rendered possible only by what may be called a " muffling " of the wings. For the flight-feathers are not only of great breadth, but they are covered, as it were, with velvet-pile, the " barbules " of the wing-quills, which form the agents by which the " web " of the quill is held together, having their upper spurs produced into long, thread-like processes, which extinguishes any possibility of a warning " swish."

John Bright, in one of his magnificent perorations, caused his spell-bound listeners to catch their breath, when, conjuring up a vision of the Angel of Death, he remarked " we can almost hear the rustle of his wings." One realizes the vividness of that imagery, when one hears, as on rare occasions one may, the awe-inspiring rustle of the death-dealing swoop of the falcon, or the sparrow-hawk, as he strikes down his victim.

But the swish and whistle of wings often stirs the blood with delicious excitement, as, when one is out on some cold, dark night, " flighting." That is to say, awaiting mallard passing overhead on the way to their feeding ground, or in watching the hordes of starlings, or swallows, settling down to roost in a reed-bed. No words can describe these sounds, but those to whom they are familiar know well the thrill of enjoyment they beget. There is no need, here, to muffle the sound of the wing-beat. The falcon vies with the lightning in his speed, escape is well-nigh hopeless : neither have the swallows need for silence ; indeed, on these occasions, they add, to the music of their wings, the enchantment of their twittering.

So much for flight in its more general aspects. Let us

turn now to a survey of some of the more remarkable forms of flight, beginning with that known as " soaring."

This but few birds have mastered, and to-day it is rarely to be seen in our islands, for eagles, falcons, and buzzards are, unfortunately, only to be found in a few favoured localities. Happily, however, one may yet realize the delight of watching a soaring buzzard, or raven, among the hills of Westmorland, or in parts of Cornwall and Wales. But to see the past-masters in the art, one must seek the haunts of pelicans, vultures, and adjutant storks. The last-named is perhaps the finest performer of them all. For the first hundred feet or so he rises by rapid and powerful strokes of the wings, and then, apparently without the slightest effort, or the suspicion of a wing-beat, he sweeps round in great spirals, gaining some ten or twenty feet with each gyration, the wings and tail all the while being fully extended and the primary feathers widely separated at their tips. During the first part of every turn he is flying slightly downward : at the end of the descent he sweeps round and faces the wind, which carries him upward. Round, round, he goes, mounting ever higher and higher, until at last he attains a height of perhaps two miles.

The adjutant thus goes aloft apparently for the mere delight the movement affords him. But not so with the vulture, who is a close rival in this art. He soars for his very

existence, **for** dead bodies are not to be found everywhere.
Possessing powers of sight infinitely greater than ours, he
mounts aloft for the purpose of taking observations. If
nothing "toothsome" can be seen from his vast range, he
turns his attention to the movements of such of his fellows
as may be up on the same errand miles away. Should he
see one swooping earthwards he instantly tracks him down,
and is soon at the feast. This accounts for the mysterious
way in which vultures will gather together to the feast, in a
place where an hour ago not one was to be seen. A caravan
of camels, perchance, is making its toilsome way across a
burning desert. One falls by the way. In a few hours its
bones will be picked clean by a horde of these ravenous
birds.

Longfellow sang the song of the vultures hunting in
stately verse :

> "Never stoops the soaring vulture
> On his quarry in the desert,
> On the sick or wounded bison,
> But another vulture, watching
> From his high aerial lookout,
> Sees the downward plunge and follows,
> And a third pursues the second,
> Coming from the invisible ether,
> First a speck, and then a vulture,
> Till the air is thick with pinions."

Darwin, in his wonderful *Journal of a Voyage Round the
World*, gives a marvellously vivid word-picture of the largest
and most interesting of all the vultures, the Condor of the

BLACKGAME

Andes—one of the largest of flying birds, having a wing-span of something over nine feet :

" When the condors are wheeling in a flock round and round any spot, their flight is beautiful. Except when rising from the ground, I do not recollect eve. having seen one of these birds flap its wings. Near Lima, I watched several for nearly half an hour, without once taking off my eyes ; they moved in large curves, sweeping in circles, descending and ascending without giving a single flap. As they glided close over my head, I intently watched, from an oblique position, the outlines of the separate and great terminal feathers of each wing ; and these separate feathers, if there had been the least vibratory movement, would have appeared as if blended together ; but they were seen distinctly against the blue sky. The head and neck were moved frequently, and, apparently, with force, and the extended wings seemed to form the fulcrum on which the movements of the neck, body, and the tail acted. If the bird wished to descend, the wings for a moment collapsed ; and then again expanded with an altered inclination, the momentum gained by the rapid descent seemed to urge the bird upwards with the even and steady movement of a paper kite. In the case of any bird *soaring*, its motion must be sufficiently rapid, so that the action of the inclined surface of its body on the atmosphere may counter-balance its gravity. The force to keep up the momentum of a body moving in a horizontal plane in the air (in which there is so little friction) cannot be great, and this force is all that is wanted. The movement of the neck and body of the condor, we must suppose, is sufficient for this. However this may be, it is truly wonderful and beautiful to see so great a bird, hour after hour, without apparent exertion, wheeling and gliding over mountain and river.

Those who " go down to the sea in ships " have to face many perils, but the " wonders of the great deep " are for them a lure. One of these is to watch the marvellous " sailing " flights of the wandering albatross. His wings have, when expanded, a peculiarly " ribbon-like " form, and measure from tip to tip, over eleven feet—thus exceeding that of the condor, which, however, is the heavier bird of the two. The " ribbon-like form of the wings is due to the extreme shortness of the flight-quills—the primaries and secondaries, and the great length of the arm and forearm. And it may be to these structural peculiarities that the " sailing " flight just alluded to is due. Resembling soaring in many of its aspects, yet it differs materially in that it is performed low down, not at immense heights. The most graphic description of these movements is surely that of Mr. Froude : " The albatross," he tells us, " wheels in circles round and round, and for ever round the ship—now far

28

behind, now sweeping past in a long rapid curve, like a perfect skater on a perfect field of ice. There is no effort; watch as closely as you will, you will rarely see, or never see, a stroke of the mighty pinion. The flight is generally near the water, often close to it. You lose sight of the bird as he disappears in the hollow between the waves, and catch him again as he rises over the crest; but how he rises, and whence comes the propelling force, is, to the eye, inexplicable; he alters merely the angle at which the wings are inclined; usually they are parallel to the water and horizontal; but when he turns to ascend, or makes a change in his direction, the wings then point at an angle, one to the sky, the other to the water."

One sometimes hears the skylark described as "soaring" upwards, when performing that wonderful musical ride which has made him so famous. But as, spell-bound, one listens to his rapturous strains, and watches his spiral ascent, one cannot help noticing that his wings are never still, they seem almost to be "beating time" to his music. In true soaring they are scarcely ever moved.

The upward progress of a bird when soaring is, of necessity, comparatively slow. But in what we may call "plunging" flight the case is very different, for here the velocity of the descent is great.

The frigate-birds of tropical seas, and the gannet of our

own, display this mode of flight to perfection. It is worth going far to see a gannet dive. Travelling at a relatively considerable height, and eagerly scanning the surface of the water for signs of a shoal of fish, this amazing bird dives with the speed of lightning, and with half-spread wings disappears with a terrific plunge beneath the surface, to emerge, an instant later, with his prey. One can measure the force of such a plunge by the cruel trick, sometimes played by fishermen, of fastening a herring to a board, and setting it adrift where gannets are about. The unsuspecting victim descends as usual upon his prey, only to meet instant death by the shock of his impact with the board. Those who talk glibly of identifying birds by their flight may point to this wonderful diver as a case in point. But while one may often see the gannet on the wing, it is by no means so often that one will have the good fortune to see him dive, for he is not always hungry. His white body, pointed tail, and black quill-feathers would then enable the novice to name him at once. But—in his immature plumage, he would, at a little distance, appear black, and unless he were fishing, the chances of recognition would be by no means great. Close at hand he would appear speckled with white.

But this by the way. There are two other birds which dive from a height on the wing. One of these is the king-fisher · the other is the tern. The term " tern " is here used

Brown Owl

collectively, for there are several species, but all have this habit of diving from a height. During the summer months one may be quite sure of an opportunity of watching the graceful, easy flight of at least three species. For they haunt the sea-shore, river, and lake with equal impartiality. Those who are on the lookout for terns, for the first time, will easily recognize them. For, in the first place, they look like miniature gulls, but with longer and more pointed wings, and forked tails. Further, all have a characteristic black cap. They travel in small parties, as if for company, keeping no more than a yard or two from the surface of the water, and scanning it eagerly in search of shoals of small fish, or crustacea. As these are found one will note a quickening of the wing-beat, and a sudden dive, like that of the gannet, with half-closed wings. And sometimes, too, the impetus will take them completely under water.

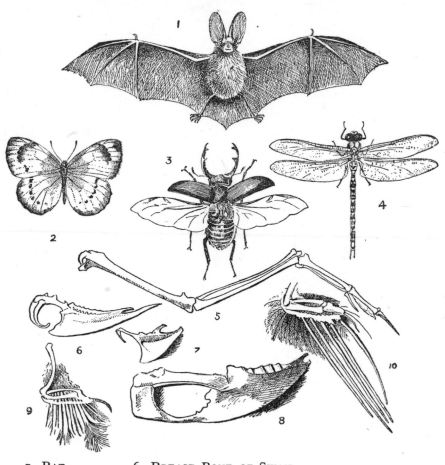

1. BAT.
2. BUTTERFLY.
3. BEETLE.
4. DRAGON-FLY.
5. BONE OF BIRD'S WING, SHOWING THE THREE DIVISIONS,
    ARM—FOREARM—HAND.
6. BREAST BONE OF SWAN.
7.   ,,   ,,   PIGEON.
8.   ,,   ,,   PELICAN.
9 & 10. APTERYX, CASSOWARY (degenerate wings).

CHAPTER IV

Modes of Flight

"The soaring lark is blest as proud
When at Heaven's gate she sings ;
The roving bee proclaims aloud
Her flight by vocal wings."

WORDSWORTH.

The movements of the wing in flight—Marey's experiments—Stopping and turning movements—Alighting—"Taking off"—Hovering—The use of the tail in flight—The carriage of the neck in flight—And of the legs—The flight of petrels—The speed of flight—The height at which birds fly—Flight with burdens —Experiments on the sizes of the wing in relation to flight—Flight in "troops."

WHILE it is possible to show that certain kinds of flight are to be associated with such and such peculiarities of the skeleton, and the muscles attached thereto, there are many "eccentricities" which cannot be measured, and explained, in terms of mechanism.

The very disconcerting, twisting, flight of the snipe is one of these. The sportsman knows it well : and he knows that the twisting, during which the bird turns the body half over—that is with, say, the left wing pointing directly downwards, and the right wing directly upwards—is only the preliminary to getting fully on the way, and that, presently, it will pursue a straight course, with arrow-like speed. Yet its cousin, the jack-snipe, never twists.

Why does the woodcock invariably drop after a charge of shot, even though not a pellet has touched it, while a snipe pursues its way? These differences are not merely differences of " habit " : they indicate subtle differences in nervous response to the same kind of stimulus, and in structural details yet to be unravelled.

Some day the cinematograph will reveal to us all the phases of flight and the movements to which they are due. Even now, thanks to the modern camera, we have learned a great deal. We have learned, for example, that the flight of a bird is not effected merely by rapid up and down movements of the fully extended wings, or with flexed wings— that is to say, half-closed, as in " gliding " flight when a bird is descending, or in the swoop of, say, the sparrowhawk. Only in one of these two positions do we ever seem to see the wings when we have to trust to our eyes alone, as the bird hurries past us. The impression that we have seen aright is confirmed when we stand on the deck of a steamer, and watch the gulls following in its wake. For incredibly long distances they will travel without a perceptible wing-beat. The albatross is the finest of all performers in regard to this kind of flight, which is due, apparently, to air currents created by stiff breezes, or gales. Some birds seem to make their way against a head-wind with the minimum of effort, by partly flexing the wings and gliding downwards : at the end of the descent, by turning the body sharply upwards, and spreading the wings to the fullest extent, they are lifted up, and driven forward, like a kite.

Marey and Pettigrew, long ago, showed conclusively, by means of photography, that our conception of the movement of the wing during flight was far from correct.

To avoid a long and tedious description, and many technicalities, it must suffice to say that the wing of a bird possesses very considerable freedom and range of movement at the shoulder-joint. Certainly, during some phases of flight, the wings are thrust forward and extended to their fullest extent, so that the outer margins of the wings come to lie almost parallel with the long axis of the body, as may be seen in the spirited illustration showing the goshawk in flight. As they sweep downwards, and backwards, they lift the body and drive it forwards. At the end of the " sweep " they are " flexed," that is to say, bent at the elbow and wrist-joints, while at the same time they are raised and brought forward above the body for a repetition of the stroke. These movements are too quick for the eye to follow, but they have been fixed for us by the camera.

Marey devised an ingenious experiment in his endeavour to discover the movements of the bird's wing during flight.

37

He fastened a small piece of paper to the tip of a crow's wing, and as the bird flew in front of a perfectly black screen he took a photograph of this moving speck of white, while, of course, no image of the crow appeared on the plate. The resultant picture gave a series of " figure of 8 loops " as one would make this figure with a pen, contriving to make the lower loop very small, and the upper loop very large. But as the wing-beat increased in speed the lower loop gradually faded out.

These movements of the wing, however, are descriptive rather of what takes place during very vigorous flight, as when the bird is getting up " steam." When he is well under way there is no need for these long and very tiring strokes, except in the case of birds like the pheasant or the duck. A gull, when in full career, does not, apparently, raise the wings very high, nor depresses them very low, nor does it flex the wings at the wrist-joints.

Stopping and turning movements are generally extremely difficult to follow, because they are performed so quickly. They can be seen fairly easily in the case of some of the larger birds. Ducks, as is well shown in one of our coloured Plates, draw the head backwards, tilt the body upward, thrust the feet forward, and spread the tail, at the same time turning it forwards. Gulls and pigeons too may be watched with profit.

Wild Duck

In turning, the body is tilted sideways, so that the tip of one wing points skywards, the other earthwards, as in the case of the goshawk illustrated in this book. The pigeon, and some other birds seem further to spread out the long stiff quills borne by the thumb, which form what is known as the " bastard-wing." This turning movement is well shown, again, in the very realistic coloured picture of the woodcock turning in mid-air, and bearing too the burden of one of its nestlings.

If it is difficult to satisfy oneself as to the way in which a bird alights, it is no less so to detect its movements in taking wing. Most of us must have seen sparrows making this effort from the road, thousands of times. But ask of any one, How is it done ? The act takes place so quickly that the eye cannot follow its execution. And what is true of the sparrow is true of most birds. But there are some where this is not the case. Many water-birds, the cormorant, for example, get under way but slowly, and with evident effort. They flap along the surface for some distance before they gain sufficient impetus to lift them into the air. And there are many long-winged, short-legged birds which can rise from a level surface only with great difficulty, or not at all. The swift is one of these, for its legs are excessively short. The albatross is another : and this is true, indeed, of many of the petrel-tribe. The puffin, again, seems unable to rise on the wing from the ground. It appears invariably to run along until it reaches the edge of cliff which lodges its burrow, and then, as it were, throw itself over the edge. The heron, when springing into the air, stretches his long neck out to its fullest extent, and presents a pair of dangling legs, well shown in one of our coloured Plates, but when once fully on the way its pose entirely changes, the neck being drawn in and the legs thrust out backwards.

Flight does not always mean progress through the air. Most birds can, at need, arrest their course, and hang, as it were, suspended in the air. In the beautiful coloured Plate, representing the chaffinch hovering over its half-fledged young, and in that of the kingfisher and its young, this form of " hovering " flight can be seen. But the greatest of all exponents in the art of hovering is the kestrel, known also, for this very reason, as the " windover." It is most fascinating to watch this bird hang, as it were, from the clouds, motionless, yet with quivering wings, as he scans the ground below in his search for some unsuspecting mouse. It is hard, indeed, to say which is the more wonderful, this power of remaining stationary for comparatively long periods in the air, or the surprising powers of sight which this bird possesses. During these hovering movements, always head to wind, it will be noted, the tail plays a very important part, being spread to its extremest limit, and at the same time thrust forward beneath the body. In some birds this forward movement is more marked than in others. And this because such birds possess a somewhat more flexible spine, there being a certain amount of "play" where the vertebræ of the loins join the welded mass of vertebræ which lie between the bones of the hip-girdle.

But the tail feathers are not indispensable. This much is shown in the case of birds like the kingfisher, the water-hen, and the land-rail, which contrive to fly well, and at a great pace, though they have but the merest apology for a tail. More than this, the grebes have no tail at all. But it is to be noted that they are by no means adept at turning movements; owing to the lack of this appendage the body, when in mid-air, has a curiously truncated appearance, as may be seen in the illustration. Further, it is significant that in the contemptible "sport" of pigeon-shooting from traps, the birds are deprived of their tails to prevent them from making turning movements.

The carriage of the head and neck, and of the legs, during flight presents some interesting, and some instructive contrasts.

Ducks, geese, and swans, flamingoes, storks, and cormorants always fly with the head and neck stretched out to their fullest extent. Herons and pelicans, though also long-necked birds, draw the head back till it rests almost on the shoulders. Most birds, indeed, fly with the head drawn back towards the body. The appearance of some of these birds on the wing can be seen at a glance on turning to the page illustrating this aspect of flight.

Not so very long ago a great controversy was waged as to what birds did with their legs during flight. Many of the older artists invariably depicted them drawn up under the breast. But as a matter of fact, this method seems to be confined to the Passerine birds—the " perching birds," such as crows and finches and their kin. It has yet to be settled what obtains among what are known as the " Picarian " birds, such as kingfishers, bee-eaters, woodpeckers, and so on. The legs and feet of these birds are so small, and their flight is so rapid, that the matter is by no means an easy one to settle. But all other birds carry the legs and toes bent backwards, under the tail. In the gulls, this can easily be seen, and easier still in the case of the common heron, where they are, as it were, trailed out behind—owing to the shortness of the tail and the great length of the leg. The puffin carries them " splayed " out on each side of his tail, and so also do his kinsmen, the razor-bills and guillemots.

The legs, as a rule, take no part in flight. True, they can be seen thrust out just before alighting, but this is solely for the purpose of effecting a safe landing. But where gulls can be watched at close quarters, as in harbours, round a

42

Sketches of Ducks in flight 1922
Roland Green

1.
1a } SCAUP

2. GOLDENEYE

4.
3. } MALLARD

5
to } POCHARD
10.

ship, or in such favoured spots as are to be found about the bridges of London during the winter, careful watch will show that the legs are frequently used when efforts are being made to turn, or check the speed of flight.

Some of the smaller petrels—like the storm-petrel, or "Mother Carey's chickens," will patter over the water with their feet as they fly just over the surface of the waves.

Whether the legs are carried drawn close up beneath the breast, or thrust backwards under the tail, the purpose of this disposal is the same—to prevent any interference with the "stream-lines" of the body which would impede flight.

On the matter of the speed of flight there seems to be much misconception. Gätke, the German ornithologist, gravely asserted that the little Arctic blue-throat—one of our rarer British birds—could leave its winter resort in Africa in the dusk of evening, and arrive at Heligoland— where he spent so many years studying bird migration— nine hours later. That is to say, it could travel 1600 geo- graphical miles in a single night, at the astounding velocity of 180 miles an hour! According to another estimate of his, curlews, godwits, and plovers crossed from Heligoland to the oyster-beds lying to the eastward, a known distance of rather more than four English miles, in one minute; or at the rate of over 240 miles an hour. Against such extravagant estimates it is hardly necessary to bring rebutting evidence.

But if any be demanded it may be furnished by the carrier pigeon, which has been known to maintain a speed of 55 miles an hour for four hours in succession : and it is extremely unlikely that this is much, if at all, exceeded by any wild bird during long-distance flights.

That our spring and autumn migrants must possess wonderful powers of endurance is beyond question. And it is equally certain that thousands must perish by the way. By this means is the standard of flight maintained—the weak perish. Even the minimum standard of efficiency for the survival of such an ordeal must be a high one.

Few of us see anything of these marvellous migration flights. For, in the first place, they are generally performed at night, and at a great height, often beyond the range of human vision. Only as they approach land, and their destination, do they descend. American naturalists have made some interesting observations by directing a telescope against the sky. Thus, Mr. Frank Chapman, by turning his instrument towards the full moon, has seen birds passing at night at an altitude, according to his computation, of five miles : while the late Mr. W. E. D. Scott saw, through an astronomical telescope at Princeton, New Jersey, great numbers of birds passing across the face of the moon—warblers, finches, and woodpeckers among them. Mr. Chapman again, on another occasion, saw no less than 262 birds pass over the field of his telescope at a height of from 1500 to 15,000 feet ; and the most remarkable thing of all was the fact that the lowest birds were flying upwards, as if they had risen from the immediate neighbourhood and were seeking the proper elevation to continue their flight.

As has already been remarked, when nearing their destination migrating birds descend, though still many miles from land. Should a gale be raging they fly so low that they barely top the waves. And this, apparently, to escape, so far as is possible, the force of the wind. Larks, starlings, thrushes, and other small birds, can sometimes be seen during daylight crossing the North Sea in their thousands. At such times many will often afford themselves a brief rest in the rigging of ships, homeward bound, but the main host hurry on. The beautiful golden-crested wren, our smallest British migrant, is one of these. A glance at our charming coloured Plate will show at once that the wing is not that of a bird of strong flight. There is no more interesting experience to the bird-lover than that of watching the tired travellers drop earthwards, as they leave the dreadful sea behind them.

With all birds yet retaining the power of flight there is always a liberal " margin of safety " in regard to the wing area. That is to say, this is always in excess of the minimum area necessary to make flight possible. This much, indeed, is manifest from the fact that the eagle can bear off a victim equalling himself in weight. Should he miscalculate, he can always drop his burden, or lessen its weight by eating part of it on the spot. Not so the osprey, or the sea-eagle, which have been known to plunge down and drive their talons into fishes too large to be raised. Unable to release their grip, death, by drowning, has inevitably followed.

Sometimes the burden is a passenger, instead of a victim. One of the most striking of the coloured Plates in this volume is that of a woodcock carrying one of its nestlings to a distant feeding-place. This habit is well known. It is not often that the necessity arises, but there are occasions where suitable nesting and feeding grounds cannot be found together, or when, as during prolonged drought, the normal feeding area dries up. Then, instinctively, the parent will surmount the dangers of starvation for their offspring, by conveying them to a land of plenty, returning again to the shelter of the wood as soon as the meal is over. The weight of a newly-hatched nestling, it is true, could scarcely be called a " burden." But they are carried about thus until they are strong enough to perform the journey for themselves. Thus, then, towards the end of the nursing period the weight to be carried is by no means a light one.

But it was shown, long since, by direct experiment, that the area of a bird's wing is considerably in excess of what is required for the purpose of flight. Dr. J. Bell Pettigrew, more than fifty years ago, to test this matter, cut off more than half of the secondary wing feathers of a sparrow, parallel with the long axis of the wing. He first clipped one, then both wings, and found that in both cases flight was apparently unimpaired. He then removed a fourth of the primary feathers—the outermost quills—and still the flight was unimpaired. At any rate the bird flew upwards of thirty yards, rose to a considerable height and alighted in a tree. Thirty yards, however, is a short flight even for a sparrow. But it is enough to show that flight, if not *sustained* flight, was possible after this mutilation. Not until more than one-third of the quills along the whole length of the wing were removed, did the flight become obviously laboured. And he found that what was true of the sparrow, was equally true of the wings of insects.

Though these experiments demonstrate, in a very unmistakable manner, that flight with a greatly reduced wing area is possible, we have no evidence that this reduction would make no difference to the length of time the bird could remain on the wing. And this is a very important matter.

An aspect of flight which has now to be considered is that of birds which fly in troops. Some species always travel thus, others only on occasions. Rooks and gulls afford instances of this, when, during windy weather, or for other reasons, they congregate and fly round and round in great circles, at a consdierable height. Small wading-birds, like ringed plovers and dunlin, commonly fly in "bunches." The last named furnish a singularly interesting sight when thus travelling; for their evolutions are so amazingly timed. As if at a given signal every bird in the troop will change its course at the same moment, and in the same direction, so that now one sees a flickering mesh-work of grey, and now a shimmering as of snow-flakes, as first the grey backs, and then the white breasts are turned towards one. But flights such as this are to be seen only during the autumn and winter months. For during the breeding season these little flocks are broken up and distributed far and wide. But there is yet another reason. They wear a totally different dress—the courtship or breeding plumage. Herein the upper parts are of a rich chestnut hue, streaked with black, while the under parts are black. Even more fascinating to watch are the autumn troops of starlings on the way to their roosting places. Hundreds at a time, not to say thousands, take part in these flights. Now they rush onward, in one great far-flung sheet, and now they close up into a great, almost ball-like, mass: and now they thin out till they look like a trail of smoke. But always they wheel and turn and rise and descend, not as separate bodies, but as one. How are such wonderful evolutions timed. The movements of an army on review-day are not more precise, or more perfectly carried out. During the whole flight not a sound, save the swishing of their wings can be heard. The marvel of it all is beyond the range of words, nor can one express the peculiar delight such a sight affords.

Why is it that ducks and geese commonly fly either in Indian file, or in a roughly V-shaped formation, with the apex of the V forward ? Why do they not fly all abreast ? One cannot say, but they never do.

Some mention must be made here of the surprising numbers in which geese, of some species, congregate. Writing of the Brent goose, in his *Bird Life of the Borders*, Mr. Abel Chapman—and there are few men who can write with such authority on the subject—tells us : " Just at dark the whole host rise on the wing together, and make for the open sea. In the morning they have come in by companies and battalions, but at night they go out in one solid army ; and a fine sight it is to witness their departure. The whole host, perhaps ten thousand strong, here massed in dense phalanxes, elsewhere in columns tailing off into long skeins, V's or rectilineal formations of every conceivable shape (but always with a certain formation)—out they go, full one hundred yards high, while their loud clanging, defiance—" honk, honk,— torrock, torrock," and its running accompaniment of lower croaks and shrill bi-tones resounds for miles around."

PEREGRINE CHASING DUCK.

51

CHAPTER V

Courtship Flights

" A pair of falcons wheeling on the wing,
In clamorous agitation . . ."

WORDSWORTH.

The wing-play of blackgame and grouse—The " musical ride " of the snipe—
The " roding " of the woodcock—The musical flights of redshank and curlew—
The " tumbling " of the lapwing—The raven's somersaults—The courting flight
of the wood-pigeon—The manakin's "castanets"—Wings as lures—The strange
pose of the sun-bittern—The " wooing " of the chaffinch and the grasshopper-
warbler—Darwin and wing-displays—The wonderful wings of the argus
pheasant.

ONE of the most striking features of bird-life is surely
its restless activity. This is always apparent, but it
attains to a state of almost feverish excitement as the spring
advances, and the parental instincts re-awaken. As they
gather strength, so they manifest themselves, in outbursts of
song—often of exquisite beauty—strange antics, or wonderful
evolutions in mid-air.

It is with these last that we are chiefly concerned here.
As might be supposed, they present a wide variety in the
matter of their form and duration. Blackgame furnish an
example of a very simple form of courtship flight, but it is
associated with curious antics on the ground. And these,

53

it is to be noted, are only to be witnessed soon after sunrise. Two blackcocks will approach one another and stand as if prepared to ward off a very vigorous onslaught ; reminding one of two barn-door cockerels. With lowered head and neck they face one another, the beautiful lyrate tail spread fan-wise, and arched so that the curled, outer feathers touch the ground, while the wings are trailed like those of the turkey-cock. Then one will at last rush forward, and seizing his adversary by the scruff of the neck, will administer a sound beating with his wings. The victor celebrates his triumph by a loud, and most unmusical screech, which has been likened, by that accomplished observer and sportsman-artist, Mr. J. G. Millais, to the call of cats on the house-tops at midnight. But presently a greyhen makes her appearance. Hostilities cease at once, on all sides ; and intense excitement prevails amongst the whole assembly—for a large number of cocks will gather together at these sparring matches. Her approach has been observed by a single bird, who, unintentionally, gives the signal by suddenly drawing himself up to a rigid position of attention, till he is sure she is really coming, then he throws himself into the air and flutters up a few feet, uttering at the same time, a peculiar hoarse note of exultation. Immediately all the others follow suit ; each seeming to strive to outdo his neighbour in a series of absurd pirouettings. Here we have a "Love-flight," of exceedingly

Roland Green

Woodcock carrying Young

brief duration, associated with terrestrial combats and frantic prancings.

The grouse pursues a different method. He strives to incite his mate to amorous moods by chasing her about. But she is " coy," and will tolerate this for hours at a time, apparently intent on nothing more than seeking something interesting to eat, she seems to affect to be quite unaware of the presence of her importunate mate ; though her behaviour is belied by the fact that she keeps up a continuous " cheeping " note, heard only at this time of the year. Every now and then he will vary his tactics by leaping up into the air and taking an upward flight of from twenty to thirty feet, crowing vociferously. On alighting he will commence his addresses again. Then, perhaps, she herself will take to flight, darting off and twisting like a snipe, evidently enjoying her tantalizing tactics. He follows in close pursuit, in the hope, doubtless, of satisfying his desires, when she shall come to rest. Here is a " courtship " flight of longer duration, in which both sexes participate.

The " musical ride " of the snipe is of a much more imposing character : and in this, again, both sexes take a part. During this performance, which affords some thrilling moments to the bird-lover, the bird ascends to a great height, and then plunges earthwards in a terrific " nose-dive " accompanied by a weird bleating noise, comparable to the bleat of a goat. For long years discussion waged furiously as to the source of this sound. Some held that it was produced by the voice : others by the tremulous motion of the wing-feathers : others, again, contended that it was caused by the tail-feathers. This was first mooted by the Danish naturalist, Meeves, and he produced some very striking and curious evidence to prove his view. He showed that the outermost tail-feathers had peculiarly thickened shafts, which were also bent in a very striking way. By removing these feathers, and sticking them into a cork, he was enabled, by twirling the cork rapidly round at the end of a string, to reproduce the " bleat " exactly. Many years later Dr. Philip Bahr revived this experiment, for the purpose of finally setting the matter at rest—for there were still many who remained unconverted to the Meeves interpretation. Dr. Bahr left no room for further doubt. He showed, too, that during the production of this sound these tail-feathers were extended laterally, so as to separate them from the rest of the tail, and so give the air rushing past them during the earthward plunge full play on these sound-producing structures. He, too, applied the test first instituted by Meeves, and so clinched his arguments. One may hear this strange music as early as February, and even, though rarely, as late as July. But it is essentially a breeding-season, or rather a " Courtship " performance sound, though it may be evoked

56

by a sitting bird suddenly surprised, when she will " bleat " as she leaves her eggs, possibly to distract the intruder on her vigil.

The woodcock has a " love-fight " but of a quite different character, known by sportsmen as " roding." It takes the form of short flights up and down the " ride," or space selected for the nesting site. But while the female is sitting the male will still continue these flights, choosing the early morning and evenings. As he goes he utters strange cries, which have been compared, by some, to the words " more rain to-morrow," and by others to " Cro-ho, cro-ho," varied by a note sounding like " whee-e-cap." These flights are varied by strange little displays upon the ground, when he will strut about before his mate with wings drooped and trailing on the ground, the tail spread, and the feathers of the head and neck standing on end. This gives him a very odd appearance, to human eyes, but it serves its purpose—which is to arouse his mate to amorous moods.

Redshank, curlew, and dunlin—cousins of the snipe and woodcock—are all accomplished performers in the art of wooing on the wing. The male redshank, uttering flute-like notes, Mr. Farren tells us, soars up to a moderate height, and remains, for a brief space, " hanging in the wind " with the tips of his curved wings rapidly vibrating. He then descends, pipit-like, earthwards, while the song, which has been uttered slowly, now quickens, reaching its climax as the bird, raising its wings above its back for an instant, finally alights on the ground. But he has yet other wiles, which are not used in mid-air. Approaching his mate with his head erect and body drawn up to its full height, he raises his wings for an instant high above his head : then allowing them gradually to droop, he vibrates them, at the same time rapidly moving his legs like a soldier " marking time."

The curlew seems to prefer the evening for his best efforts. Rising from the ground with rapid wing-beats, he will " check " suddenly when near the summit of his ascent ; so suddenly as almost to throw himself backwards. Then, recovering, he will hang poised, kestrel-like, in mid-air, and pour forth a joyous thrilling, or jodelling, song. Rising and falling, on quivering wings, or sweeping round in great circles, and hovering again, he will remain for some considerable time pouring forth this joyful ripple of song.

The courtship flight of the lapwing is even, if possible, more interesting. Rising from the ground with slow heavy flaps of his broad wings—which, it is to be noted, present a remarkable difference from those of the female, in that the primaries are much longer, so as to give this portion of the extended wing a conspicuously broader appearance—as though he had difficulty in getting under way, he speedily dissipates this impression by a sudden upward rush, an

58

LAPWINGS

height, each striving to get above the other for a downward swoop. As the one "stoops" at the other, the lower bird dodges, and so rapidly are the wings moved that they are often brought smartly together over the back, producing a clapping noise.

Even the black, forbidding raven has his amorous moods. And at such times he will even outdo the more lively, though irascible lapwing in the art of aerial somersaults; if somersaults they can be called. For in the middle of an ordinary spell of flying he will suddenly fold up his wings and bring them close up to the body, at the same time turning completely round, as though he were turned on a spit; the body being held horizontal as the turn is made. For a moment or two there he is suspended, as it were, between earth and sky, with his back towards earth, and his breast towards the heavens. Lest he should forget the manner of the trick, it would seem, he will practise it at times, during the stern work of chasing intruders from his territory; for he will brook no competitors on his ground.

The wood-pigeon, during the courtship season, makes frequent sallies into the air for the purpose, apparently, of giving vent to his exuberant feelings. During such flights he will dart up from the tree-tops and sail round, high above, in great circles, rising and falling as he goes, with outspread wings, every now and then bringing them over his back with a resounding snap. During such displays the white bar across the wing is most conspicuous, serving at once to identify the performer.

Among our native birds, the only other species which habitually, and especially during the courting season, produce characteristic sounds during flight, by bringing the wings smartly together over the back, is the nightjar. But there are certain small passerine birds, known as manakins, inhabiting the forests of South America, which have the shafts of the quill-feathers of the forearm enormously thickened. By means of these transformed and translated "castanets," at will, the bird can produce a sound which has been likened to the crack of a whip.

So far this discourse has been concerned solely with "courtship" flights, or flights associated with peculiar sounds, dependent on rapid movements of the wing in mid-air for their production. And with the mention of these instances this chapter might, quite legitimately, be brought to an end. But it must not. And this, because there are a number of birds which put their wings, during Courtship season, to very different purposes. Spectacular flights and evolutions in mid-air do not appeal to them. They use their wings instead as lures, as a means of adding intensity to strange poses and pirouettings ; whereby they desire to give expression to the amorous feelings which possess them, in the hope—if for the moment, we may accord to them human standards of intention—of arousing kindred emotions in their mates.

Darwin was the first to draw attention to these curious displays. Which, on the evidence then available, seemed always to be made, and only to be made, by birds having wings conspicuously coloured. It seemed as though the possessors of such wings were conscious of their beauty, and so displayed them that nothing of their glory should be missed.

The sun-bittern affords a case in point. This bird, a native of Brazil, is soberly, but very beautifully coloured when at rest ; its plumage presenting an indescribable mixture of black, grey, brown, bay, and white ; blended in the form of spots, bars, and mottlings. But during times of sexual excitement it will spread out its wings in the form of a great fan, encircling the long, slender neck. And in this position they present a very conspicuous appearance, taking the form of beautifully graded bands of black, white, and bright grey, forming patterns which vanish the moment the primaries fall into their place behind the quills of the forearm. But when thus spread the bird seems to find the greatest delight in displaying their chaste splendour before his mate. He seems to spread his wings just because he is conscious of their beauty when thus opened out.

But we need not travel so far as Brazil to find examples of displays of this kind. Among the birds of our own Islands we can find many close parallels. The chaffinch and the goldfinch, when seeking to arouse the sympathy of their mates, make much play with their wings, not only in short "nuptial flights," designed, apparently, to display the conspicuous and brilliant colouring of the plumage as a whole, but when perched on some convenient spray. At such times the wing is more or less completely spread out, as if to reveal, to the fullest possible advantage, the bright bars and splashes of colour which this extension alone can bring into being.

Since these gaily coloured vestments seemed always to be associated with striking, stilted attitudes, sometimes bordering on the grotesque, and always to be paraded in the presence of the female, Darwin drew the inference that they were the outcome of female choice persistently exercised during long generations. That is to say, he held that, far back in the history of the race, these performers were soberly clad, as their mates commonly are. Then certain of the males of these now resplendent species began to develop patches of colour, small at first, but gradually increasing, generation by generation, in area and intensity. This progressive splendour, he believed, was due to the "selective" action of the females, which, from the very first, chose from among their suitors those who stood out among their fellows by reason of their brighter plumage. Thus the duller coloured males died without offspring. On this assumption each succeeding generation would be, in some slight degree, brighter than the last, until the process of transformation ended in the glorified creatures we so admire to-day.

It would be foreign to the purpose of this book to pursue this theme at length. Let it suffice to say that while the "Sexual Selection" theory still holds good, it has, so to speak, changed its complexion. And this largely owing to the accumulation of new facts. For the most important of these we are indebted to the singularly exact and laborious observations analysed, clarified, and interpreted with remarkable insight and sagacity of Mr. H. Eliot Howard, one of the keenest ornithologists of our time. He has set forth his case, and interpreted his facts with masterly skill, and there seems no escape from his conclusions. Briefly, he has shown that birds of quite sober coloration like the warblers, which formed the basis of his investigations, engage in displays quite as remarkable, and of precisely the same character as in birds of gaily coloured plumage. From this it is clear that this wing-play is not prompted by a more or less conscious desire to display conspicuously coloured patches of colour, for of colour there is none save that of the general hue of varying shades of brown, as in the case of the grasshopper warbler, for example. Nor is the display, apart from colour,

Herons

to be regarded as a performance slowly perfected through long generations through the selection of females, coy and hard to please. We must regard these " Nuptial flights " and wing-displays as the outward and visible signs of a state of ecstatic amorousness on the part of the males which, by their persistence and frequent recurrence, at last arouse sympathetic response in the females. They play the part of an aphrodisiac. Without them there would be no mating. In my *Courtship of Animals* those who will may pursue this subject further.

Before closing this chapter mention must be made of the most remarkable wing-display to be found among birds, and of the equally remarkable uses to which they are put. The possessor of these wonderful appendages, for they are wonderful, is the argus pheasant of the Malay Peninsula and Borneo. Though efficient for short flights in jungles, all that is ever required of them, they would be quite useless in open country where an extended journey had to be made, or escape attempted from some vigorous enemy. And this because the secondary wing-quills—the quills attached to the forearm—are of enormous length, making, as we have remarked, sustained flight impossible. They have, indeed, come dangerously near losing their normal functions altogether. And this because they have passed over into the category of specialized " secondary sexual characters." But for the fact that this bird lives in an environment where food is abundant all the year round, and can be obtained without any undue exertion, and that there are no serious enemies to be evaded, it would long since have become extinct. For this exuberant growth of quill-feathers must be borne all the year round, though they are not required to function in their later rôle, save during the period of courtship.

Their great length is not their only striking feature, or even their chief feature. This, indeed, is represented by their extraordinary coloration. For each feather bears along its outer web a series of " ocelli," so coloured as to look like a series of dull gold balls lying within a deep cup. Outside the ocelli run numerous pale yellow longitudinal stripes on a nearly black background. The inner web is of a delicate greyish-brown hue, shading into white and relieved by innumerable black spots, while the tips of the quills have white spots bordered with black. The primaries, too, are most exquisitely coloured, though in the matter of size they are not very exceptional. These, indeed, are the only true flight feathers.

The full beauty and significance of the coloration of these feathers can only be appreciated during periods of display. Then the two wings, in some indescribable manner, are opened out so as to form a huge circular screen, concealing the whole of the rest of the body. The effect produced from the human standpoint is one of great beauty, after the first burst of astonishment has spent itself. His mate is less easily moved. Perchance " familiarity breeds contempt." At any rate it is only after persistent and frequent attempts to charm her to his will that success rewards him.

Those who have the good fortune to be able to make frequent visits to the Zoological Gardens in London may, with great good fortune, and at rare intervals, have an opportunity of witnessing such a display, and of studying in detail these wonderful wings. They are wonderful, not merely because of the manner of their display, or of their colouring, but also because in them we see ornament pushed to its furthest limit since, as wings, they have become well-nigh useless, and therefore almost dangerous to the well-being of their possessors.

SUN-BITTERN DISPLAYING.

CHAPTER VI

How to tell Birds on the Wing

"I can tell a hawk from a hernshaw."

SHAKESPEARE.

The small perching-birds and the difficulty of distinguishing them—The wagtails—The finches—The buntings—The redstart, wheatear, and stonechat—The thrushes—The warblers—The tit-mice—The nuthatch and tree-creeper—The spotted flycatcher—The red-backed shrike—Swallows, martins, and swifts—The nightjar—Owls—Woodpeckers.

THE experienced ornithologist apart, there are hosts of people who are interested, at least, in our native birds : who would fain call them all by name ; yet who can distinguish no more than a very few of our commonest species. They are constantly hoping to find some book which will give, in a word, the "Hall-mark" of every bird they may meet in a day's march. But that book will never be written. For some species present no outstanding features by which they may be certainly identified, when no more than a momentary examination is possible, and this at a distance. And it is often extremely difficult to set down in words, exactly, what are the reasons for deciding that some rapidly retreating form belongs to this, or that, species.

And then, too, there are difficulties due to seasonal changes of plumage—often striking—sex, and age ; since immature birds often differ totally from the adults in appearance. The young robin and the starling afford instances in point.

The adult starling, as everybody knows, is " black," with a yellow beak and reddish legs. But seen close at hand his feathers gleam with a wonderful metallic sheen reflecting changing hues of violet, green, and purple. The young bird, in the early summer, is of a pale brown colour. In the autumn the plumage is changed for a " black dress," like that of the adult, but heavily spotted with white. As the winter wears on the white spots become abraded, and disappear. The robin needs no description. But the young bird, in its first plumage, is commonly mistaken for the female, which, of course, is practically indistinguishable from the male. It is certainly unlike one's notion of a " cock-robin," being of a yellowish-brown colour, with pale spots, a type of plumage characteristic of the young of the " thrush tribe."

In some nearly related species, again, the males are strikingly different, the females barely distinguishable.

But nevertheless, a very considerable number of our British birds can be more or less easily distinguished during flight—sometimes by the manner of that flight, sometimes by characteristic markings, sometimes by the notes they utter ; and these are briefly summarized in this chapter.

1. Swallow   5. Pied Wagtail   9. Goldfinch
2. House Martin   6. Grey Wagtail   10. Linnet
3. Swift   7. Yellow Wagtail   11. Greenfinch
4. Sand Martin   8. Chaffinch   12. Bullfinch

When it is realized that no less than 475 species, and sub-species, of British birds are now recognized, it will be apparent that it would be impossible to do more than briefly epitomize the commoner species, and some of these, like the robin and the wren, need no interpreter.

The aim of this chapter is primarily to give, as far as possible, the salient features of our commoner native birds, as seen during flight. But some species merely " flit," from one place to another, and that so rapidly that no details of coloration can be distinguished. They can only be examined at favourable, and often fleeting moments, when at rest, and clear of foliage. Only such as are frequently encountered are included here. To attempt more would be to lead to confusion. Enough, it is hoped, will be said to help the beginner. Experience will soon lead to an ever-increasing proficiency — and with this will come an ever-increasing conviction that the identification of birds, during flight, is an extremely difficult task. Whoever essays it should, whenever possible, supplement his efforts by the aid of a pair of good field-glasses. These, indeed, are indispensable.

The small perching birds are, perhaps, the most difficult to name at sight, and this because their flight presents so little to distinguish one species from another. All fly with rapid wing-beats, alternating with a period during which the wings are practically closed, causing the body to travel

73

forward on a rapidly descending curve in the interval between the wing-beats. This gives rise to what is known as an "undulating" flight. But the large passerines, like the crows, differ conspicuously in their method of progress. With them the wing beats relatively slowly, so that its shape can be readily seen ; and their course is direct—hence the familiar saying "straight as the crow flies." Further, the inner webs of the outer primary quills are, what is called "emarginate," that is to say, the width of the web is suddenly reduced towards the tip of the feather, so that the outstretched wing has a conspicuously fringed appearance, as may be seen at a glance at the beautiful pen-and-ink sketches on another page. The eagles and falcons have similar emarginations.

But to return for a moment to the smaller passerines. There are very few of our native species which could be distinguished in the field by their flight alone. For the most part one has to rely on this and clues afforded by characteristic markings : while a further aid is afforded by at least a slight knowledge of the haunts of birds. One would not expect to find a wheatear in a wood, or a wren in a reed-bed.

The wagtails are among the easiest of the "undulating" fliers to distinguish, if only because of the great length of the tail. The pied-wagtail, with its black and white plumage—or black, grey, and white in the winter—can be identified at a glance. And so, too, may the yellow and the grey wagtails. The last named has the longest tail of all, and is further marked by his beautiful grey back and bright sulphur abdomen and under tail coverts. All have white feathers in the tail. The pipits and skylarks, like the wagtails, have very long inner secondaries, but they can never be confused on this account. They can never be mistaken for wagtails, but on the other hand, the several species can be distinguished, when on the wing, only by long practice.

The chaffinch, greenfinch, and goldfinch are with us all the year round, keeping each to his favourite haunts. Most people know them well. But one meets even people living in the heart of the country who cannot call them by name! The cock chaffinch can be distinguished at once by its white " shoulders," and white bars across the wing, apart from the bright hues of the body, so well shown in the adjoining Plate. The hen has similar wing-marks, but lacks the bright colours of her lord. His cousin, the brambling—who comes to us in the winter—is just as easily identified by his orange-coloured shoulder patch—in place of white—and white rump, which is most conspicuous during flight. The greenfinch is marked, when in flight, by the yellow rump and bright yellow patches at the base of the tail-feathers. Who could mistake the goldfinch for any one else but himself ? He looks like a butterfly as he flutters about on the tops of tall thistles.

The crimson and black bands on his head, the glorious blaze of gold on his black wings, which are further marked with white spots, as also is his tail, make him the most gorgeous of our native finches. The bullfinch, again, is easy to distinguish ; though from his habit of haunting thickets and dense hedgerows, he is seldom seen. In flight you may know him by his white rump, rosy breast, and black head. But his mate is more soberly clad : though her black head and white rump will suffice to make sure of her when, by good fortune, she is encountered.

One of the commonest of what we may call " roadside " birds is the yellow-hammer ; which can be recognized at once by the bright yellow colour of its head. As soon as it takes to flight the white feathers in the tail and the chestnut rump will make assurance doubly sure. But in some parts of England one meets with another, and similar species—the cirl bunting. In this species, however, the male has a black throat and ear-coverts, and an olive-grey chest-band ; while the female, lacking these distinctive marks, may be recognized by a brown, instead of a chestnut rump. When in the neighbourhood of swampy places and reed-beds, a look-out must be kept for the reed-bunting. A small bird with a black head and throat, and white collar, this is the male. The female will display a brown head, buff throat and eye-brow, and white outer tail-feathers. In the winter time, near the

Chaffinch and Young

sea, one may frequently come across the snow-bunting, which, on the wing, will at once attract attention by the large areas of white displayed in the wing and tail.

The redstart, one of our summer visitors, is a bird which can never be mistaken. A sight of the russet-red tail alone suffices. But the cock has the further glory of a mantle of grey, a black head and russet under parts. He is fond of country rich in old timber, or hillsides, where stone walls attract him. His kinsman, the wheatear, returns to us in the early spring; to give an added charm to our bare hill-sides, and warrens, sea-cliffs, sand-dunes, and waste places. If you see a small bird flying low over the ground, with a white rump, and black wings, you may know that the wheat-ear is before you. That delightful, restless little bird, the stonechat, is a near relation of the wheatear. He, too, is fond of waste places, and heaths ; more especially such as will provide him with plenty of furze bushes, or ling, on the top-most twigs of which he loves to perch, flitting his tail and uttering his fussy little notes, " hweet-chat, hweet-chat." On the wing you may tell him by his conspicuous white wing-patch, and the broad blaze of white on his neck, set off by a jet-black head. The female and young lack the bright chestnut on the breast. The stonechat's cousin, the whin-chat, may be found in similar situations, but he is of a more roving disposition, and may be found also in lowland pasture and water-meadows. More slender in form, he is further to be distinguished by the dark streaks down his back, white-eye stripe, and greater amount of white at the base of the tail. Further, there is no white neck patch.

Most people know the common thrush and the blackbird when they see them, and many country-folk, indeed, recognize no more. Yet there are five species in all, which may be called " common." They are to be distinguished, not so much by their flight, as by their general coloration. Neither the common thrush, nor the blackbird need be described here : they cannot easily be confounded with any other bird. But for the moment it might be possible, it is true, to mistake the missel-thrush for the more common song-thrush. It is, however, an unmistakably larger bird, and when on the wing appears greyer, and if seen at close quarters, shows white tips to the outermost tail-feathers, and a white underwing. On the ground, of course, there can be no mistaking it, on account of its much more spotted breast ; the spots, too, being much larger, and fan-shaped. During the autumn and winter there are two other thrushes which should be looked for. These are the fieldfare and the redwing. The first-named, it is to be noted, will be found in small flocks, and if examined on the ground through field-glasses will be seen to have a slate-grey neck and rump, and chestnut-brown wings and tail ; while the breast is streaked instead of spotted.

78

In flight the underwing is white, as in the missel-thrush, from which it can easily be distinguished by its smaller size, and the absence of white on its tail. The redwing, like the fieldfare, is gregarious. This is an important point to bear in mind; since it might otherwise be confused, by the novice, with the song-thrush, the two being about the same size. But seen at rest, close quarters, there can be no mistake; the redwing having a conspicuous cream-coloured eye-stripe, and chestnut-red flank-feathers. The underwing is similarly coloured. Finally there is the ring-ousel, which haunts the moorlands and rocky ravines. But it may be recognized at once by its conspicuous white gorget, contrasted with its otherwise black plumage.

Of the forty species of British warblers there is not one which the most expert of our ornithologists would venture to identify by the character of the flight alone. Most of these species, of course, are rare and accidental visitors; many need an expert to distinguish them, since they represent but Continental races of our own summer visitors. About ten species can be called common, or fairly common, in suitable localities, and the novice must not expect to recognize even these with anything like certainty. They have no characteristic flight, and they rarely do more than " flit " from one place to another. In the pages of this book, then, they can rightly have no place. But some may, perhaps, be glad of a few notes concerning one or two of the commoner species. The black-cap, for example, may be readily distinguished by its grey plumage contrasting with a black cap—reddish-brown—in the female. It has also a peculiarly delightful song, which some prefer to that of the nightingale. This, the most celebrated of all our warblers—though for some inscrutable reason some ornithologists appear to regard it as a near ally of the redstarts and robin !—frequents woods with thick undergrowth and tangled hedgerows, and hence is seldom seen, but may be recognized by the uniform russet-brown coloration of its upper parts, shading into pale chestnut on the tail, and the ash-grey of the under parts, shading into white on the throat and abdomen. The whitethroat may be recognized by the fine white ring round the eye, grey head, brown upper parts, and buffish-pink breast, set off by the conspicuous white throat, from which the bird derives its name. It is perhaps the only British warbler which can really be distinguished during flight, and this only because the outermost pair of tail-feathers are almost wholly white. It may be looked for in hedges and thickets, as well as on gorse-covered commons. Its near relation, the lesser-white-throat, differs in its smaller size, whiter under parts, and the absence of the rufous edges to the secondaries, which are one of the distinguishing features of the common white-throat. The garden-warbler is much more frequently heard

1. Sea Gull
2. Hooded Crow
3. Gannet
4. Golden Eagle
5. Snipe
6. Redshank
7. Nightjar
8. Barn Owl
9. Rook
10. Cuckoo.

than seen, its song, a continuous, sweet, and mellow warble, rivalling that of the blackcap, though softer and less varied. Haunting shrubberies and gardens, it is yet the mere ghost of a bird, its uniform brown upper parts, and brownish-buff under parts, coupled with its shy, retiring disposition make it exceedingly difficult to see. Three other tantalizing little members of this numerous tribe are the chiffchaff, willow-warbler, and wood-warbler. Tantalizing because so frequently seen during the summer months, so much alike, and yet, somehow, different. The novice has no name for them ; the expert can only tell them by a combination of characters, and their contrasts. He is guided rather by their notes and habits, than by their appearance, so closely do they resemble one another ! The chiffchaff, as its name suggests, is to be identified by its song—Chiff-chaff, chiff-chaff, chiff, chiff-chaff-chiff—uttered from the top of a high tree. The singer is too small to be seen, so that he who would discover what manner of bird is the songster, must watch in the direction of the sound, till the singer elects to descend. The willow-warbler is a rather larger bird with a tinge of yellow in his plumage. Also it is less restricted to woods and coppices, and has a sweet, indescribable warble. The wood-warbler is the largest of this trio—from the tip of his beak to the tip of his tail he may measure as much as five inches—and is also the most brightly coloured. Above he is greenish, with

81

an eyebrow of sulphur yellow, and a sulphur-yellow breast and throat. Since he is rarely to be found, save in woods of beech and oak, he will, on this account, the more easily be distinguished from his cousin, the chiff-chaff and the willow-warbler. This fact, again, can be taken into account when the identity of one or other of these two is in question.

The warblers are essentially birds of the countryside—they cannot abide the busy haunts of men, who seem unable to settle anywhere without setting up hideous tramways and ugly buildings. Kindly Nature is crowded out. The garden, hedgerow, and shady woods are the chosen haunts of the warblers, though some prefer the reed-grown stream, or the thickets round quiet pools. The reed and the sedge-warbler will be found here, but by no means easily so, for after the manner of their tribe they love seclusion. To find the reed-warbler you must go to reed-beds, or to osier-beds, and there watch for a little bird, chestnut-brown above, and white below. But for this constantly babbling chatter—" churra, churra, churra "—you would never, probably, find him. Guided, however, by his song, you may succeed in finding him nimbly climbing up and down the reed stems. Very like him is the rarer marsh-warbler : but, for your guidance, note that the marsh-warbler has a really melodious song, and is even more likely to be found in swampy thickets of meadow-sweet than the reed-beds. The sedge-warbler, though showing a decided preference for streams fringed by osier-beds and thickets, is more of a wanderer than the other two, since tangled hedgerows, and thickets, at a distance from the water will often suffice him. You may know him by the fact that he is of a dark brown colour above, streaked with a paler shade of brown, while the under parts are white, tinged on the breast and flanks with creamy buff.

Ornithologists rarely concern themselves with anything but the superficial characters of birds. Not even the structure of the feathers interests them, but only their coloration. Hence it is that they have come, quite commonly, to regard the gold-crest, or " gold-crested wren," as it is sometimes called, as one of the tit-mouse group! There is not even the remotest justification for this view. It is an indubitable warbler. A glance at the coloured Plate will render any description of its appearance unnecessary. From autumn to spring you may find it in most parts of England and Scotland—save the extreme north—hunting in hedgerows and woods for food. During the breeding season it favours coniferous woods. Along the south and east of England, one may also meet with a closely similar species—the fire-crest. But while in the gold-crest the crown is of a bright lemon-yellow, in the fire-crest it is of a bright red-orange hue, while the side of the head is marked by a white stripe bordered with black.

The gold-crest is our smallest British bird. The ranks of our resident " gold-crests," in the autumn, are swollen by immigrants from northern Europe, who seek shelter with us because unable to withstand the rigours of the more northern winter. In the matter of size the gold- and fire-crested wrens agree, measuring but a trifle more than three and a half inches from the tip of the beak to the tip of the tail! By the way, the shape of the beak should be carefully noted. It is that of a typical warbler.

It may be urged that this description of the warblers might well have been omitted from these pages, since, in regard to " Flight," nothing whatever can be said, save that they " fly." There would, indeed, be some justification for such criticism, but it is to be remembered that this volume is written, not for the expert, but for the novice, who, because he needs a few concrete examples of the hopelessness of expecting to identify every bird he may encounter by its flight, and of the methods he must occasionally adopt, when seeking to name a bird which will not come out into the open. His course of training, and discovery, will be much shortened by the realization that birds by no means always reveal their presence by taking long flights.

What is true of the warblers, in this regard, is true also of our numerous species of tit-mice. We do not distinguish between them in the field by their flight, but by their coloration.

But since these are such confiding little birds, coming to our very windows during the winter months, for food, a few notes concerning them may be acceptable. The commonest of all is the little blue-tit, or "tom-tit," as it is so often called. Its beautiful cobalt-blue crown, blue back, wings, and tail, white face, and yellow breast are familiar to us all. Its larger relative, the great tit-mouse—the largest British tit-mouse—bears a close general resemblance to the smaller species, but is readily distinguished, not only by its greater size, but by the broad band of black running down the abdomen. Its flight, as of all the tit-mice, is weak and, as it were, uncertain, confined to short passages from tree to tree. The coal tit-mouse and the marsh tit-mouse are seldom recognized as distinct species, by the novice. They are very soberly coloured little birds, the coal-tit being of an olive-grey, tinged with olive-buff, while the sides of the body are buff : the head and throat are black, relieved by a broad patch of white on each side and down the nape of the neck. The marsh-tit is, to all intents and purposes, of the same coloration, but differs conspicuously in lacking the white patches. The tiny longtailed-titmouse cannot possibly be mistaken for any other bird. Its delicate hues of pink and grey, and extremely long tail, make comparisons with any other species unnecessary.

Where, during the winter, small birds are tempted to

85

come to a tray of nuts and seeds, placed outside the window, that charming little bird the nuthatch—a near relation of the tit-mice—will commonly be among the guests. It cannot be mistaken for any other British bird, its form and coloration being alike distinctive. Its upper parts are of a delicate blue-grey, its under parts buff, passing into chestnut on the flanks. The throat is white, while there is a black line from the beak to the eye, and beyond, spreading as it goes. A relatively large beak, and strikingly short tail, are features as conspicuous as is the coloration. Its flight is slow and undulating.

Another little bird which, during the winter, associates with the tit-mice is the tree-creeper. It is never seen on the wing, save when it is flitting from one tree to another, and then its course is obliquely downwards—from the upper branches of one tree to the base of another. This it proceeds to ascend immediately on alighting, by jerky leaps. Its coloration is soberness itself—mottled brown above and silvery white below. The tail, it is to be noted, is formed of stiff, pointed feathers, like those of the woodpecker, and, as in that bird, is used in climbing.

There is scarcely a garden—save in such as are within the area of a big town—which, during the summer, is not haunted by a little grey and white bird, with a most characteristic flight—a sudden sally into the air to seize some insect, some-

Roland Green

Gold Crested Wrens

times even white butterflies, and an instant return to the same perch. This is the spotted flycatcher. In Wales, Devonshire, Cumberland, and Westmorland, one may be fairly sure of meeting with the pied-flycatcher. He is, so to speak, a black and white edition of his relative, the spotted flycatcher—but the black areas in the female are represented by brown. There are, however, notable differences in the method of hunting, in the two species; for the pied-flycatcher rarely returns to the same perch after his upward flight into the air, and he often feeds on the ground.

In the straggling hedgerows of the wooded districts of south and central England, and in Wales, one may often come across the red-backed shrike; a very handsome bird, with pointed wings, long tail, and low swooping flights. His red back will alone distinguish him. No other British bird wears such a mantle. And this is set off by a grey crown and nape, and black patches on the sides of the head. The topmost twig of a bush, or hedge, where he can sight his prey from afar, are his favourite perches. On the east coast of England, during the autumn, one may sometimes see the great grey shrike, distinguished readily by his large size, fan-shaped tail, and grey coloration, relieved by black ear-coverts, black wings and tail, " blazed " with white, and white under parts. His flight is undulating and irregular, while just before alighting he gives a peculiar upward sweep.

Strangely enough, not only country boys and girls, but their fathers and mothers, not only confuse swallows and martins with one another, but these with the swift! Yet they are readily distinguishable. All, it is true, have long, pointed wings, and forked tails : but their coloration is very different. The swallow has the most deeply forked tail of them all, and his steel-blue back, red throat, and rufous buff-and-cream under parts are unmistakable identification marks. The martin may be distinguished at once by the conspicuous white rump patch, and pure white under parts. These are the signs by which they may be recognized when on the wing—and they are more often seen thus than at rest. The sand-martin is a much smaller bird, has a less markedly forked tail, and is of a uniform pale brown above, and white below, but with a brown band across the chest. The swift is not even related to the swallow-tribe. On the wing—and very few people ever see him otherwise—he is very different. The wing-beat is extremely rapid and intermittent, while in its shape the wing differs in its extreme length and narrowness. The flight is extremely swift—hence the name of the bird. Not its least impressive feature is its wonderful flexibility. Who has not watched, with delight, a troop of these birds sweeping down the village street, now skimming the ground, now sweeping upward and away, round the church tower, accompanied by wild, exultant screams, as though

88

they were bubbling over with vitality. When high up they look like so many animated bows and arrows—the arrows being, perhaps, somewhat short and thick. The swift, it is worth remembering, is a near kinsman of the humming-bird, which also has a long narrow wing. Both alike agree in this peculiarity—an upper arm-bone of excessive shortness, and a hand of excessive length. No other birds approach them in this. The only other bird which has wings quite so ribbon-like, when extended, is the albatross—one of our rarest British birds. But here the proportions of the wing are reversed, for the upper arm-bone is of great length, while the hand is relatively short.

There is something inexpressibly soothing about the twilight of a summer's evening. Most birds are abed. The swift can be heard high up, the " woolly bats, with beady eyes," are silently flitting all round one, turning and twisting as no bird ever turns. But for the chorus of the swifts, like black furies, and heard only at intervals, and faintly, all is silence, relieved, perchance, by the drowsy hum of a blundering dor-beetle. Then, suddenly, if one be near some gorse, or bracken-covered common, the stillness is broken by a strange " churring," like a bubbling whistle, rising and falling in volume. This may be followed by a loud " clap." And yet the source of these strange notes cannot be located, nor can any living thing be seen to which they could be attributed. But keep careful watch. Presently there may emerge from the gathering gloom a long-winged, long-tailed bird, travelling at speed, with a twisting flight, and deliberate wing-beats, alternating with long glide on motionless pinions. As it passes one may notice white spots on wings and tail. This is the nightjar : a bird of ill omen among the aged inhabitants of the countryside, for they will assure you that it is guilty of sucking the milk of cows and goats. Hence, it is commonly known as the " goatsucker." Poor bird, it is quite innocent of such misdeeds, for though it has an enormous mouth, armed on either side with long bristles, it feeds only on moths and beetles.

If you are fortunate, your vigil in the gloaming may be rewarded by a sight of yet other night-birds. Out of some hollow tree, or swooping round the barn, may come a ghostly form, borne on absolutely silent wings : but with a reeling, buoyant flight, which is unmistakable—this is the barn owl. If you are *very* fortunate, you may hear its blood-curdling screech. Once heard you will never forget it ! His cousin, the tawny owl, it is whose musical, if doleful " hoo-hoo-hoo-hoo-o " has so commonly been misrepresented by poets—and others—as " to-whit-tu-woo." Its flight is slower and its wings rounder than in the barn owl, and furthermore, it lacks the glistening satin-white under parts of that bird.

But its coloration and general appearance are well shown in the coloured illustration.

The other species of owls we may reckon as fairly common residents with us. They are the long and the short-eared owls. But they are very rarely to be seen on the wing in daylight. Each has the habit, when excited, of bringing the wings together smartly over the back, so as to produce a sound likened by some to the word " bock."

Few birds have figured so largely in our literature, perhaps, as the cuckoo. Though heard by all, he is seen by few : and this because so many people fail to recognize the charming wastrel when they see him. In general appearance he recalls the sparrow-hawk. I have known even gamekeepers confuse the two. But the cuckoo is much paler on the back, and the bars of the breast are finer. On the wing he is much slower than the sparrow-hawk ; his wings are shorter, and his tail is tipped with white. Immature birds may be recognized by their clove-brown coloration, and a large white patch at the nape of the neck.

One of the most brilliantly coloured of all our native birds is the kingfisher. Small streams and quiet pools are its favourite haunts. A glance will suffice to identify it at close quarters, but even if one catches sight of its fleeting form at too great a distance to see its wonderful coloration, it can be distinguished by its extremely rapid and direct flight, and curiously shuttle-shaped form : an appearance due to the shortness of its tail, as may be seen by a reference to the excellent coloured Plate.

The identification of birds in flight will be rendered easier for the novice if he makes a practice of " expecting " to find particular birds in particular places. That is to say, the haunts of birds are governed by their stomachs—they must not stray far from the source of their food. In a wood, then, you may " expect " to find woodpeckers—though you will often be disappointed, for they are by no means always to be seen. But the task of identification will be easier if one has a mental picture ready of the birds appropriate to the place.

The green woodpecker, our largest native species, often betrays itself by its remarkable cry, reminiscent of a laugh— " ha, ha, ha," and " pleu, pleu, pleu." Keep quite still, and presently, as likely as not, it will suddenly make its appearance with a rapid, undulating flight. As it alights on some neighbouring tree-trunk, its identity will be finally established by its green back and wings, yellow rump, and crimson crown. It ascends the tree by jerky leaps. Where ant-hills abound it may often be seen on the ground, moving about with awkward hops, exploring the hills for ants. The greater and lesser spotted woodpecker may also sometimes be seen here, especially if there is much old timber about. In spring its presence is often made known by a peculiar

Rabnier Grann

Great Spotted Woodpeckers

drumming sound—never forgotten when once heard—made by excessively rapid blows with its beak on the trunk, or branch, of a tree. On the wing it may be recognized by its "dipping" flight, and strikingly piebald appearance. At close quarters the strongly contrasted black and white plumage is relieved by crimson undertail-coverts, and a crimson crown. The lesser-spotted woodpecker is a much smaller bird—about the size of a sparrow, or chaffinch—and is barred with black and white ; there is a patch of crimson on the head of the male. It has a habit of keeping more to the upper branches of the tree than the other species : but, like its greater cousin, it "drums" on the tree during the spring, but less loudly. Its spring cry, "pee-pee-pee," is like that of the wryneck. This is a near relation of the woodpeckers, but very different in coloration, being beautifully mottled and vermiculated with grey and brown. But for its spring cry, just alluded to, it would escape notice altogether, so closely does it match the bough it is perched upon. Uu like the woodpeckers its tail-feathers are not developed to form stiff, pointed spines. This is accounted for by the fact that, though it ascends tree-trunks readily, it does not hammer at the bark with its beak, and so does not need stiff tail-feathers to afford leverage. Its flight is slow and hesitating, It is commonest, it may be remarked, on the south-east of England.

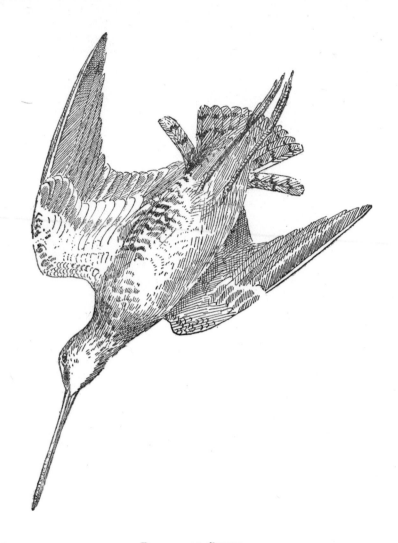

DRUMMING SNIPE.

95

CHAPTER VII

How to tell Birds on the Wing

(continued)

"The seamew's lonely laughter
Flits down the flowing wave ;
The green scarts follow after
The surge where cross-tides rave."

FIONA MACLEOD.

Falcons—Golden eagle—Harriers and sparrow-hawk—The heron—The cormorant, shag, and gannet—The petrels—Guillemots, razor-bills, and puffins—The ducks—The great-crested grebe and dabchick—The pigeons—The " plover tribe "—The gulls and terns—The game-birds.

OUR native birds of prey, the owls and hawks, have been so harassed by gamekeepers that many species are now exterminated, while others are but rarely seen. Some, however, in favoured localities still remain to us. At one time the owls and hawks were believed to be nearly related : they were distinguished as the " Nocturnal " and " Diurnal " birds of prey. We now know that they are not in the remotest degree related. The owls, indeed, are closely related to the nightjars. They have been already discussed here. The hawk tribe must now have their turn.

The one most commonly seen to-day is the kestrel, which

97

spirals, holding its broad wings almost horizontally, and spread so that the primaries stand widely apart for half their length, and in this joyous movement they will remain aloft for hours on end.

But for the untiring efforts of the Royal Society for the Protection of Birds, none of our larger birds of prey—save, perhaps, the golden eagle, which is carefully cherished in the deer forests—would now be left to us. The case of our harriers seemed hopeless. But, thanks to a zealous protection, a remnant remains.

The harriers are in many ways extremely interesting birds. In appearance, when closely examined, they present one remarkable feature. And this is found in the curious arrangement of the feathers of the face which radiate from the eye as a centre, as in the owls, to form a " facial disc." They are all large birds, of slender build, and have a habit of flying close to the ground with their long, slender legs dangling, crossing and recrossing the same area till they are sure they have examined it thoroughly. Frogs, eggs, small birds, and voles form their principal food. Every now and again they will rise and circle round at a considerable height, seeking a new feeding-ground.

The marsh-harrier is our largest harrier, and has rounded wings and slower wing-beats than the others, from which it is further readily distinguished by its chocolate-brown coloration, cream-coloured head, and grey tail and secondaries, which contrast strongly with the black primaries. The hen-harrier breeds only in the Orkneys and the Outer Hebrides. It is distinguished by its grey coloration and pure white rump patch. Montagu's harrier is a somewhat smaller bird, and has black bars on the secondaries. In flight it is more graceful and buoyant than its relatives, and this is accomplished by three or four wing-beats, alternating with a long glide on half-raised pinions. It, again, nests annually in East Anglia, thanks to protection.

There remains but one other bird of prey to mention here, and this is the sparrow-hawk. It may be easily recognized during flight by its short, rounded wings and long tail. The female, which is much larger than her mate, has the under parts distinctly barred. The breast of the male is similarly marked, but the bars, being of a pale rufous, or rust colour, and much narrower, are less conspicuous. It has a very rapid and gliding flight, just above the ground, or along hedgerows, which it scours in its search for small birds.

There may be many who will fare forth to find the harrier on the wing. If they succeed they will indeed be fortunate. But there is one bird that most certainly will be seen in the "harrier country," and that is the heron. There can be no mistaking him. He may be found, a large, grey bird, standing contemplative, knee-deep by the river's margin, or in some ditch, awaiting the moment to strike at some unwary fish, frog, or water-vole. The moment he discovers that he is being watched he will be on the move. He rises heavily, almost awkwardly, with flapping wings and outstretched neck : his legs dangling down. But no sooner is he well on the way than he hauls in his neck till the head is drawn close to the body, and straightens out his legs till they extend behind him like a pair of streamers. Henceforth his flight is easy and graceful enough. This is the bird which was so much prized in the old days of " hawking." The invention of the gun ended this most fascinating form of sport.

Let us turn now, for a little while, from moor and wood and fen, to the seashore, and, for choice, to a rock-bound coast with towering cliffs. Here you will find a number of species which will never be found inland. They love the sea, whether it be shimmering in the sun of a blazing June day, smooth as a mill-pond, or in a fury of thundering billows, lashed by a roaring gale in bleak December. The bottle-green shag is one of these. You cannot mistake him. Perched on a rock he sits upright, and, in the spring, wears a crest upon his head. On the water he floats with the body well down, and every few moments disappears with a spring into the depths, for his never-ending meal of fish and crabs. His flight, just above the water, is strong and rapid. His cousin, the cormorant, is a conspicuously larger bird, with a

1. Partridge.
2. Gannet.
3. Whitethroat.
4. Red-Backed Shrike.
5. Magpie.
6. Goldfinch.
7. Great Crested Grebe.
8. Buzzard.
9. Puffin.
10. Grey Wagtail.

bronze-coloured plumage. In the breeding season his head has a hoary appearance, due to the presence of numerous filamentous feathers, known as "filoplumes"; while the throat is white, and there is a large white patch on the thigh. He has a habit, after a full meal, of sitting on some convenient perch with wings spread wide open and open-mouthed, apparently as an aid to digestion. But he is by no means so wedded to the sea as the shag. Rivers and inland waters will serve him as well as the sea.

The gannet, though very nearly related to the cormorant, is a bird of very different habits and appearance. When adult it is snow-white in plumage, with blue beak and feet, and can be mistaken for no other bird. Its peculiar mode of fishing was described in Chapter II.

Finally, there are two most interesting features of these birds which are worth remembering. To wit, the toes are all enclosed within one web, and they have no nostrils, and but the merest apology for a tongue.

And now we come to the petrels. These are for the most part nocturnal birds, spending the day in burrows. They would, therefore, find no place in these pages but for the fact that one may occasionally be seen at sea when one is fishing off the shore in a boat. The commonest is that known as the Manx shearwater. Rather larger than a pigeon, it may be distinguished by its flight, which is rapid; the wings presenting periods of rapid quivering, alternating with long sailing with fixed, widely spread, narrow pinions. At one moment one sees only the deep black of the back, the next the pure white of the under parts as the birds turn now this way, now that, holding the outstretched wings at right angles to the surface during the turn, so that one wing barely misses the waves, while the other points skywards.

Sometimes, too, one may see the little " Mother Carey's chicken." A tiny sprite, sooty-black in colour, and with a white rump patch, it often flies so close to the water that it is able to patter along the surface with its feet as it flies.

The fulmar petrel is indeed a child of the sea, for, except in the breeding season, it never comes to land. But at sea you may have the good fortune to see it off the east coast of Great Britain, and the north and west of Ireland—and in winter off the south and west coasts of England. Though in coloration resembling a common gull, it may always be distinguished, when on the wing, by its narrow wings, curved like a bow—not sharply angled as those of a gull, and the primaries are not black-tipped. Its flight is strong and powerful : slow wing-beats alternating with long glides. On far St. Kilda, in the breeding season, you may find them in great hosts. For some unexplained reason they are increasing in numbers, and may now also be found breeding in the Shetlands, Hebrides, and Orkneys.

Some who read these pages may, perchance, be stimulated by a desire to enlarge their acquaintance with our seabirds by spending a day at sea in a small row-boat. For choice, one of the larger breeding-stations should be visited. Horn Head, Donegal; St. Kilda, the Scilly Islands, the Bempton cliffs, Yorkshire; the Farne Islands, Fowlsheugh, Stonehaven; the Orkneys, the Shetlands, or the Hebrides, are all renowned resorts. Here are thrilling sights indeed. Guillemots, razor-bills, and puffins are congregated in swarms, which must be seen to be believed. Few birds are more easy to tell at sight as they scuttle past one on the way down to the water from the cliffs, or returning laden with food for their young. The puffin is easily the most conspicuous, since he flies with his little yellow legs stuck out on each side of his apology for a tail. And for a further token there is his great red and yellow beak. The guillemot has a sooty-brown head and neck—in his breeding dress—slate-grey back and white under parts, and a pointed beak; while the razor-bill, similarly coloured, is to be distinguished by the narrow white lines down his highly compressed beak. By good fortune, the white-winged black guillemot may be found among the host. His white wings contrasting with the black plumage of the rest of the body, and his red legs, suffice to identify him.

On the Farne Islands, as well as on the Orkneys and

Shetlands, you may be sure of finding the Eider duck, one of the most singular, and most beautiful members of the duck family. It is singular because of its coloration; the under parts of the body being of a velvet-black, while the upper parts are white, thus exactly reversing the normal distribution of these " colours." The rosy hue which suffuses the forepart of the breast, and the bright green patch on the cheek, make up an unforgettable scheme of coloration. The female is very soberly clad, being of a dark brown, barred with black. A further and valuable identification mark is furnished by her beak, which, like that of her lord, seems unusually long, owing to the sloping forehead. The flight is slow and close down to the water.

The sheld-duck is another strikingly coloured species that is commonly seen on sandy shores and estuaries. There can be no mistaking it. On the wing it has a conspicuously pied appearance, while the flight seems slow and rather laboured. Seen at rest, and fairly near, a broad chestnut band across the breast, and a black band down its middle, will be noticed, while the black head and neck are admirably contrasted with a coral red beak. The legs are pale pink. In winter, on parts of the east coast, they sometimes form flocks of several hundreds. The heavy-bodied, black ducks, one often sees scurrying along, close to the water, sometimes in immense flocks, are common scoters. The male is entirely

1. Peregrine Falcon
2. Kestrel
3. Merlin
4. Golden Eagle
5. Montagu's Harrier
6. Goshawk
7. Osprey
8. Sparrow-Hawk

black, with an apricot-yellow beak-patch, the female is a dark brown, with grey cheeks.

Though the duck tribe is represented by a considerable number of species, the number likely to be seen by the casual wanderer is very few ; for these birds mostly keep well under cover during the day. In addition to the three species just described there are at least two others which are not infrequently seen, out in the open, during the day. One of these is the goosander, which, on the lochs and rivers of Scotland, is common ; and it is also frequently encountered in similar situations in the northern counties of England. You may know him by his bottle-green head, which bears a crest, black back, and white wings. His breast is suffused with a wonderful pale salmon colour—which fades away within a few hours of death, leaving the breast white. The beak is long, pointed, and coral red. Moreover, its edges are armed with horny teeth ; for he is a fish-eater, capturing his prey by diving. On the wing he is very fast, but he rises from the water but slowly. His mate has a reddish-brown head and neck, and a grey back. The second species referred to is the mallard, though it is only very occasionally, and by accident, met with during the day. Its appearance has been so well represented in the coloured Plate that there is no need for description.

When on the margins of lakes, large ponds, or slow-moving

other bird impossible. One is also sure to find the ringed-plover. A little bird with a pale brown back, a white forehead with a bar of black above it, black face, and a black band at the base of the white neck. The beak is short, and the legs yellow. The wings, in flight, are long and pointed, and marked with a white bar. The outer tail-feathers, spread during flight, are also white. It runs rapidly about, swiftly picking up sand-hoppers and other small creatures, and always travels in small flocks. Commonly associated with the ringed-plover one finds the dunlin, grey above, white below, and with a long, black beak. The peculiarities of its flight, and its strikingly different summer dress have already been described here. Sometimes you will meet with the common sandpiper ; a small bird, about the size of a thrush, who runs on rather long legs, and constantly flicks his tail up and down. His coloration is of a bronzy-brown, above, more or less conspicuously marked with darker bars, and white below. In flight he shows long, pointed wings, and a tail broadly tipped with white and barred with black. More often you will find him on the banks of streams. His cousin, the redshank, a much larger bird, has already been described here in regard to his spring love-making. Later in the year he may be distinguished, when on the wing, by the large white rump patch, white secondaries, white tail, barred with black, long, pointed wings, and long red legs.

The wary curlew, already referred to, is really a moorland bird, but spends the autumn and winter by the shore, or on the mud-flats of estuaries. His peculiar cry, a shrill " *cour-lie*," readily distinguishes him. Added to this is his large size, brown coloration, and long curved beak. On the wing, the rump and upper tail-coverts are conspicuously white.

The " waders," sometimes collectively referred to as the " plover-tribe," are represented in the British Islands by a very long list of species, of which only the commonest are mentioned here. Many, however, are mere casual visitors. Near allies of this " tribe " are the gulls and terns. The peculiarly graceful, elastic flight of these birds surely needs no description. Even town-dwellers know them well. For during the winter months they follow the rivers far inland. Even in grimy London they may be seen in hundreds during the winter months. The black-headed gull is by far the commonest of these winter visitors. But at the same time, to the uninitiated, the name " black-headed " must seem singularly inappropriate ; for its head is emphatically *white*. At no time, indeed, is it ever *black*. But keep careful watch of the hosts which throng the river from January onward, till they depart for their breeding quarters, and you will see them gradually developing a dark patch on each side of the head. And this slowly spreads till the whole head is of a dark, sooty-brown. Immature birds may be picked out by

BUZZARD SOARING.

wrist-bones may be found. And the " palm-bones," which in the adult are welded together, are here quite separate. This stage, then, carries us back towards the ancestral, reptilian fore-limb used for walking, or perhaps for climbing. And there is another sign of this earlier reptilian period to be found in such a wing. At the tip of the thumb and first finger in unhatched ducks, game-birds, and water-hens, for example, you will find a small claw. By hatching time the claw of the first finger will have disappeared, but it is still retained in the case of the duck and the water-hen. In the adults of all three you will rarely find more than the claw of the thumb : and this now serves no useful purpose whatever.

Indeed, there seem to be only two tribes which have any use for wing-claws during nestling life. One of these is represented by the gallinules, that is to say, the coots, and water-hens, and their kind. You may test this whenever you have the good fortune to capture a young water-hen. Place him outside the nest, and especially if it happens to be a little raised, you will see him make his way back, using feet, wing-claws, and beak. His wings, it will be noticed, at this stage are used as fore-legs. The other tribe is represented by that strange bird the hoatzin of the Amazon. Here the two claws are really large, and they play a quite important part in his early life.

For the young hoatzin is hatched in a nursery—a crude

Grouse

nest of sticks—placed on the boughs of a tree overhanging the water. As soon as hatched he begins to climb about the branches. Should he fall, by some mischance, into the water, he promptly swims to the bank ; and by the aid of his long first finger, and wing-claws, and his huge feet, soon climbs back. But the most wonderful part of his story is yet to come.

So long as these youngsters can only scramble about they are in constant jeopardy. A wing-surface at least big enough to break the force of a fall is an urgent necessity. And so the growth of the quill-feathers is, so to speak, pushed forward with all possible speed. But if all the feathers grew at the same rate, there would speedily come a time when the outermost feathers would make the claw at the end of the finger useless, while the wing-surface, as a whole, would be insufficient. To obviate this difficulty, the development of the outermost feathers is held in abeyance till the inner feathers of the hand, and the outermost of the forearm, have grown big enough to suffice to break the force of the fall. As soon as this stage is arrived at, the outermost quills, whose growth has been held in abeyance, rapidly develop ; the finger decreases in length, and its claw disappears, while that of the thumb soon follows suit. And thus it comes about that the hand, in the nestling, is relatively much longer than in the adult. But in its mid-period it may be taken to represent the adult stage of the wing of the ancient Archæopteryx. This bird could have been but a poor flier, and probably during the time it was moulting its quills it was absolutely flightless, so that it needed a permanent finger-tip, and claw, beyond the margin of its wing-surface.

This matter of " moulting," by the way, needs, at least, passing comment. All birds renew their plumage at least once : the body plumage often twice in the year. The old feathers fall out, and their places are taken by new ones. But their growth is slow. In geese and ducks, and some other birds, the wing-quills are moulted all at once, so that flight, for a week or two, is impossible. But they can escape from their enemies while thus at a disadvantage, by taking to the water. In all other birds the quills are moulted, and renewed, in pairs : so that at no time are they left flightless.

But this by the way. Let us revert, for a moment, to the hoatzin's wing. The appearance of the outermost quills of the hand, it will be remembered, is delayed till the inner feathers have grown long enough to " flutter," at least for a short distance, then the growth of the complete series proceeds apace. This has been called an " Adaptation " to enable these youngsters, active from the moment they leave the egg, to move about in comparative safety. But it is more than this. It is a survival of an ancient order of things which takes us back to the first known birds.

This is certainly a very remarkable feature, but it gains an added interest from the fact that it has a parallel in the history of the development of the wing in the game-birds. If you look carefully at the downy chicks of the pheasant, or even at barn-door fowls, you will remark that the wing-quills develop with surprising rapidity : so that they have feathered wings while the rest of the body is still down-covered. This enables them the more easily to escape prowling foxes and other enemies. In young ducks exactly the opposite condition obtains, the body is fully feathered long before the feathers of the wings appear. And this because they do not need to fly when danger threatens, but take to the water instead. But to return to the chicks of the pheasant. The wing of the chick develops at a very rapid rate. Within a few hours after hatching, the first traces of the coming flight feathers can be seen, and presently a large wing is covering each side of the tiny body. At this stage many often die. The wings, which can then be examined at leisure, reveal an extremely interesting condition. For they repeat the features which obtain in the wing of the nestling hoatzin : inasmuch as the outermost quills are also, as yet, non-existent ; and there is a free finger-tip. But it is not nearly so long as in the hoatzin, and there is no terminal claw. Surely, from this, we may infer that the delayed development of the outer quills is a survival of a time when the ancestors of the pheasant were arboreal, and hatched their young in trees. Otherwise all the wing-quills should develop at the same time, and at the same rate. Here, then, is another instance of what can be learned of the past history of a bird by a careful scrutiny of the nestling. Sometimes we shall find our evidence in the wing, sometimes in some other organ. The sequence of plumage affords abundant evidence of this. But that is another story.

So much for the " intensive " study of the wing. A brief reference must now be made to the constantly repeated statement that nestling birds are " taught " to fly by their parents. There is no evidence whatever to support this belief : and much that goes to show its improbability.

Failing more suitable sites, sand-martins will often elect to build their nests in the crevices of the masonry of bridges.

From the mouth of this substitute for a burrow is often a sheer drop of many feet to the stream below. When the nestlings, fully fledged, leave their nursery for the first time they must either " fly " from the moment they take the first plunge from the masonry, or die. Failing to make the appropriate movements of the wings nothing can save them from a watery grave. There can be no " teaching " to fly. Indeed, death no less certainly awaits every house-martin when it plunges into space from the edge of the nest. The appropriate wing-movements, necessary to produce flight, in short, are "instinctive." Those with defective instincts are forthwith killed by falling to the ground. They leave no offspring to inherit their defects.

Perhaps the most convincing evidence of all as to the "instinctive" nature of flight, in nestling birds, is furnished by the mound-birds, of the Malay Region and Eastern Australia.

These extraordinary birds lay their eggs in heaps of decaying vegetable-matter, or in the soil near hot springs; and there leave them to their fate. They lay very large eggs, it is to be noticed, so large that the growing chick finds nourishment enough within the egg to enable it to pass the ordinary nestling stage while still within the shell. By the time it emerges it has both grown and shed its first coat of nestling-down, and has developed long wing-quills. Having burst its prison walls it wriggles its way up through the loose earth to the light of day, ready to fight its way in the world unaided. Here, then, there can be no question of "teaching" the young to fly.

But some birds, at least, do, indeed, receive instruction when on the wing. And in such cases, it will be noticed, their food can only be captured by dexterous movements in full flight. For a day or two, for example, young swallows simply practice flight, to exercise and strengthen their wings. They are fed by their parents when at rest. The next step comes when they are fed on the wing, taking their food as they hover on trembling pinions from their parent's beak. In a little while the food is dropped as the parent passes, and the youngsters are made to catch it as it falls. From thence, onwards, they have to do their own hunting. The clumsy ones must die. Eagles and hawks, in like manner, teach their young to capture swiftly moving prey by dropping food to them in mid-air. If one fails to catch it the parent swoops down and seizes the hard-won meal before it reaches the ground ; then mounting aloft with it, drops it once more, till, at last the required dexterity is gained.

GULLS.

125

CHAPTER IX

Flightless Birds

" And first, I praise the nobler traits
Of birds preceding Noah,
The giant clan, whose meat was Man,
Dinornis, Apteryx, Moa."

COURTHOPE.

The steamer duck—The owl parrot—The flightless greeb of Titicaca—The dodo and solitaire—The ostrich tribe—The penguin's wings.

THE poet who penned the above lines thought more of rhymes than of reasons—as Poets so often do. What were their " nobler traits " ? He omits to mention them. None of them were ever carnivorous : and the Apteryx could by no stretch of the imagination be called a " giant." The one outstanding feature which does distinguish these birds he fails entirely to appreciate—and this is their flightless condition.

A flightless bird is an anomaly. Yet there are some who profess to believe that this state affords us an insight into the early stages of the Evolution of the wing. As a matter of fact it demonstrates the exact opposite—its degeneration.

How is it that birds ever came to such a pass ? A study

of living flightless birds, and birds that are well on the way to this condition, will afford us a ready answer.

Whenever we find birds living, so to speak, lives of languorous ease—where there are no enemies to be evaded, where there is an abundance of food to be picked up on the ground all the year round, and the climate is kindly, there flight is no longer practised. Year by year, generation after generation passes by, and no use whatever is made of the wings. In all such cases these once most vital organs dwindle away, and finally vanish. We can trace every step in this process of decay.

We may begin with the " steamer-duck " of the Falklands. In this species, after the first moult, the power of flight is lost for ever. Among living birds only a few species, apart from the ostrich-tribe, are in this dolorous case. The owl-parrot, or kakapo, of New Zealand, is one of these. A grebe found only on Lake Titacaca, perched high up a mountain-side, is another. In both these birds the keel of the sternum is represented by the merest vestige, the breast-bone being reduced to the condition found in the ostrich-tribe.

The two giant pigeons, the dodo, and its cousin the solitaire, afford instances where the loss of flight has been followed by extinction, owing to the invasion of their haunts, through the agency of man, by pigs and other domesticated animals, which destroyed their eggs and young.

The ostrich-tribe is peculiarly interesting, owing to the fact that their wings present a really wonderful series of degenerating stages.

The wings of all differ conspicuously from those of other birds in the great length and looseness of the texture of the feathers. Those of the African ostrich are the largest of all ; but they are quite useless for the purpose of flight, though they are used as aids in running. In the South American ostrich, or rhea, they are also large, but again useless for flight, for the " quill-feathers " are very weak, and have no " web," such as one finds in the quills of flying birds. And besides, the muscles of the wing have degenerated, the breast-muscles having become reduced to mere vestiges.

In both the African and South American ostriches, the skeleton of the wing, compared with that, say, of a swan, would seem, to the inexpert, to be quite normal. But with the cassowary, the emu, or the apteryx matters are very different. Here, at the first glance, it is apparent that the process of decay is far advanced ; for the bones of the hand have, as it were, shrunk up, so that a mere stump is all that remains. The wing of the cassowary is further remarkable for the fact that some of the forearm quills, or " secondaries," are represented by long, stiff quills, resembling spines of a porcupine ; the " vane " of the feather, which normally runs down each side of the shaft, has vanished altogether.

What part they play in the bird's life-history it is impossible to say. They certainly cannot be used as weapons, and they as certainly are not " ornaments." In the extinct moas the wing had still further degenerated. In some species no more than a stump of the upper arm bone was left, and in others not only this, but even the shoulder-girdle had vanished, so that only one pair of limbs remained.

Another remarkable flightless bird is the penguin. Here the wing has changed its form to assume that of a paddle; superficially identical with that of the whale, or the turtle, or that of the extinct sea-dragon ichthyosaurus. These paddles have been " re-modelled," so to speak, to enable them to be used for what we may call flight under water. Most birds which swim under water use the legs for propelling the body; but the penguin uses his paddles instead. The paddle of the turtle has similarly evolved out of a fore-leg used for walking on land. The common tortoise may be taken as the type of this leg. In the river and pond tortoises the stumpy foot of the land-tortoise gives place to a broad, webbed foot. In the turtles this webbed foot gives place to the paddle.

After what has been said about the penguin it is instructive to turn to the wings of the auk tribe—the guillemot, razor-bill, and puffin. These are very efficient for normal flight, but they are equally efficient for use under water.

CASSOWARY   PENGUIN

OSTRICH   KIWI

For these birds swim as penguins do, when submerged. Why, then, did the penguin suffer the loss of the use of his wings for flight ?

This question leads to another. Why did that giant razor-bill known as the great auk become flightless ? It would seem that its wings somehow failed to keep pace with the growth of its body, so that while they remained sufficient for flight under water, they became useless for flight in the air. Its failure in this led to its extinction, for it was unable to escape from its arch-enemy, man. When the old-time sailors, somewhere about one hundred years ago, discovered its haunts in Iceland could be profitably invaded for the purpose of collecting feathers, and bait, they speedily wiped out the race ; for being flightless they were unable to escape the marauders once they had effected a landing. Unhappily there was no Bird Protection Society in those days to stop this senseless slaughter.

Here our survey of Birds on the Wing ends. It began with flight through the air, it ends with flight through the water. It is not a little surprising, surely, to find that the same wing can be efficiently used for both these extremes of motion. And still more surprising to find that, this being so, the penguin should have been forced, so to speak, to adopt the expedient of evolving a paddle ; and so forgo the power of aerial locomotion. The skeleton of this wing, it was pointed out, differed in no essential from that of the typical avian wing. In some points, however, it has changed conspicuously. For the bones have become greatly flattened, and the several parts of the wing—arm, forearm, and hand—can no longer be bent upon one another in the Z-shaped fashion of normal wings, while the " quill " or " flight-feathers " have been reduced to so small a size that they are unrecognizable.

VULTURES.

133

PRINTED BY
MORRISON AND GIBB LTD.
LONDON AND EDINBURGH